CRASH

CRASH

The limits of car safety

NICHOLAS FAITH

B🌿XTREE

In association with Channel Four Television Corporation

First published in Great Britain in 1997 by Boxtree
an imprint of Macmillan Publishers Ltd
25 Eccleston Place, London, SW1W 9NF

Associated companies throughout the world

ISBN 0 7522 1192 7

Copyright © Nicholas Faith 1997

1 2 3 4 5 6 7 8 9 10

A CIP catalogue entry for this book is available from the British Library

Text design and typesetting by SX Composing DTP, Rayleigh, Essex
Printed and bound in Great Britain by Mackays of Chatham plc, Chatham, Kent.
Jacket Design by Slatter-Anderson
Plate section design by Design 23
Jacket photograph courtesy of Mirror Syndication International

Crash by Nicholas Faith is based on the television series 'Crash' produced
for Channel 4 by Darlow Smithson Productions Limited.

Contents

Acknowledgements

Like its predecessor, *Black Box*, the publication and writing of *Crash* depended greatly on the benevolence of Peter Grimsdale and Sandy Holton at Channel 4 and, above all, on the mass of material furnished by the makers of the series under John Smithson and David Darlow. They and their team – Liz Dobson, Peter Bate, Caroline Hecks, Steve Connelly, William Hicklin, Erika Dodd, Ulla Streib, and the incomparable Daphne Walsh who transcribed the interviews with her usual speed and accuracy – were far more patient with me than I would have been with them given their schedules. The manuscript was edited with extraordinary speed and deftness by Hazel Orme, and, for the fifth time in as many years, Susanna Wadeson and Katy Carrington at Boxtree, Macmillan, put up with my moods with the equanimity and professionalism of nurses calming a tiresome infant. Thank you all.

Introduction

Within a few minutes of the crash that killed Diana, Princess of Wales, the Paris police had erected barriers designed to prevent voyeurs from gawping at the scene. Even before the police were aware of the identity of the victims involved, they knew that any crash attracts a crowd, and that such an extraordinary, indeed almost unimaginable, event (as it would soon become apparent) would bring in onlookers by the thousand.

Our attitude towards car crashes of any description is ambiguous: we stare, but we remain uneasy at our own interest, so it was natural for there to be an inordinate and unbalanced outcry at the film of J. G. Ballard's novel *Crash*, a genuine, if genuinely unpleasant, hymn to the pornography of violence. The film merely reflected the book, but it gave rise to the sort of hysterical disapproval normally reserved for paedophiles – and the lurking feeling that it had stirred something nasty in the subconscious of those who disapproved most loudly, whether they had seen the film or not. The suggestion that they might get some sexual kick from seeing an accident triggered violent reactions.

For all our interest in car crashes – the way we slow down to peer at a crash on the opposite side of the road, our guilty fascination with the bodies, the wreckage, the machinery of recovery – we are not prepared to think very hard about the underlying issues of road and car safety, even though (and perhaps because) they touch us so frequently. There cannot be many whose family and intimate circle of friends has not been involved in a crash serious enough to injure one or more of the car's occupants. But, typically, a survey conducted by the Automobile Association about the factors we considered important when buying a car showed that injury prevention ranked lower and accident avoidance higher among drivers than security. In other words, we seem prepared to think about avoiding an accident but not about what might happen if we had one.

Not surprisingly, then, our fascination with road accidents is not matched by any real interest in road safety. We simply prefer not to think about it. If you examine the motoring section of your local bookshop you will find innumerable volumes on motor-racing, on individual makes of cars past and present, but barely any work on safety, apart from the manuals for learner drivers. The handful of relevant books is tucked away in the relatively inaccessible psychology or sociology section.

The paucity of books devoted to road safety is matched by the relatively modest effort that goes into research on it. Dr Alison Smiley, of Human Factors North, Toronto, says, 'Far more effort and money is put into endocrine diseases that very few people have, as compared to traffic safety which affects a huge number of people.'

Of course, the basic reason why we don't want to think about road safety is that we are only too aware that driving should be safer than it is, for pedestrians and other road-users as well as the occupants of a particular vehicle. Most of us are aware, if only subconsciously, that in a lifetime of driving, we can be expected to be injured at least once, but familiarity breeds not so much contempt, as a profoundly rooted lack of desire to know more about safety.

Why can we not tell ourselves to keep to the rules (or most of them) and keep our eyes on the road?

It makes matters worse that so many men – and, as we see in Chapter 8, a growing number of women as well – use driving to express themselves, define their personalities. This phenomenon is particularly noticeable in Germany, with the horrifying contrast there between the normally well-structured lives of its citizens and their refusal to accept any speed limit on their beloved autobahns. And for self-expression, read: an aggressive disregard for everyone and everything else on the road.

It does not help attempts to consider road safety rationally that accidents are relatively few and far between. As John Adams, Professor of Geography at University College, London, puts it: 'I suppose the great mystery if you stand and look at traffic is not why there are so many accidents but why there are so few. We all drive monitoring our environment for signs of danger, and most of the time we're successful in avoiding it. And when there is an accident the results are so unpredictable.'

Everyone concerned professionally in dealing with crashes can remember their sheer haphazardness. Typically, Malcolm Westwood, a fire-fighter with the West Midlands Fire Brigade, describes how he's seen 'some amazing things, incidents where a child's sucked underneath the car and round into the mud wing and you think, Good God, nothing can actually survive this – only to find that when the fire-fighters have taken the wheel off the child has just popped out. It's a miracle and the guy goes hi and the little chap goes hi. It's an amazing thing, but then you go to the next one, the humble shunt on the little side road, and there's somebody tragically killed.' He remembers another incident when a Ford Orion 'was smashed to smithereens, the roof was completely flat, the doors were closed and it had rolled over and over. We've checked it out and we're certain there's somebody tragically injured inside. Then this guy tapped on my shoulder and he said, "Well, if I was you, mate, I think I'd do so and so," and I said, "Oh, thank you very much for your help, sir, but would you just step to the back?" But he was most insistent that we did the right thing. And I eventually realized that he was the driver.'

People describe car crashes wrongly as a modern epidemic, a plague, as the major scourge of the twentieth century. Of course, death on the road – for drivers, passengers and multitudes of hapless pedestrians – has become a major killer in industrialized countries, a truly modern way of death, replacing older plagues like cholera and tuberculosis. But these deaths do not constitute an epidemic: they are simply an ever-present part of life in any economically advanced society. But, as Daniel McCarthy, a road safety officer for Devon, points out: 'There are lots of other ways of dying that seemingly we accept quite readily. Death on the roads is considered unacceptable yet far fewer people die in this way than from tobacco or alcohol. So the whole question is what is an acceptable number of deaths from a self-indulgent activity? I suppose the problem largely with driving is that many of the deaths are of people who are clearly not responsible. I think we are very good at hiding road death. We give the job of clearing them up to professionals whose horror stories we never want to hear, so maybe that's how we cope with it, that's how we balance the books in terms of making the unacceptable acceptable.' To put it more fancifully, we do not want our 'love affair' with the car extinguished by thoughts of the financial, let alone the human cost, involved.

Indeed car crashes are so much part of our everyday lives that we seem resigned to their inevitability, which, more than any other factor, seems to me the biggest enemy of any attempt to reduce their number. John Whitelegg, Professor of Environmental Studies at John Moores University in Liverpool, says: 'There's a fundamental psychology in most people, which goes back to wartime – if the bullet has your name on it – that seriously terrible things don't happen most of the time to most of us and if they do, well, that's it, your number's up . . . I think a fundamental aspect of human psychology is to reject information and evidence of danger. If we worried every day about nuclear power, road traffic accidents, BSE and everything else that comes along, then we wouldn't go out. It's a human instinct to reconstruct the information that we get so that it reinforces what we want to believe and I think this is where the car has successfully colonized human psychology. We see and accept all the positive things, the mobility, the freedom, the power, and we reject all the negatives because we just don't want to know, so the car wins hands down. We're just not generally aware of the problems it causes.'

Yet, Gerald Wilde, Professor of Psychology at Queens University, Kingston, Ontario, says: 'Because we do it so often, driving is one of the riskiest activities in life. Until the age of forty-four, roughly, the car is the most likely instrument to take us to our death. It's only later that other causes of death become more frequent.' Road traffic accidents account for up to 80 per cent of accidental deaths in the 15–24 age group. Cars are often responsible for more deaths than wars: in Britain the black-out imposed in 1939 ensured that, even with far fewer vehicles on the road, road deaths soared in the two following years, and more deaths were reported from car crashes than from the fighting during that period. Similarly, during Ulster's quarter-century of Troubles, more deaths have been reported from road accidents than from the civil war.

Above all, and most obviously, as Alison Smiley points out: 'We've gotten accustomed to how many fatalities there are on the road and we wouldn't accept that in any other mode of transportation. In the United States there are forty thousand fatalities a year. Just imagine if you had a hundred aircraft crashes a year – the outcry about that would be enormous and yet it's the same number of people. For some reason we accept it on the road but we don't accept it elsewhere.'

When it comes to travel by air or rail, we assume an unattainable perfection of total safety. When it comes to driving we assume that something awful may happen. So we make an inordinate, disproportionate fuss when an aeroplane or a train crashes, but we accept the death toll on the roads as part of the human condition. (I am writing this shortly after a train crash in which six people died, fewer than are killed every day on the roads in Britain but which remained in the headlines for a week or more.)

Where other forms of transport are concerned the public assumption that safety was important and a practical proposition was recognized early on. Britain's railway inspectorate, for instance, was founded almost as soon as the lines were laid, maritime safety became a government concern in the late nineteenth century, and as soon as the public took to the air a highly effective official structure was established to control aircraft, and those who produced and piloted them. But those who made and drove cars considered themselves independent of outside control, above all by government, which has had important effects, discussed in Chapter 11.

The story of road safety, road accidents, their causes and means of preventing them, is so complex that it can be approached in many different ways – psychological, technical, economic, industrial and so on. There is also a fundamental linguistic point involved. Even today, as Dr Burgess, a consultant orthopaedic surgeon at the Cowley Shock Trauma Hospital, in Baltimore, points out, 'The standard term in this country is still a car "accident" but those of us who are working politically are trying to change the thinking somewhat, so that it isn't thought of just as a capricious event that happens out of fate. Many "accidents" are crashes that could have been avoided by proper training of the driver, by not abusing substances, by having a vehicle that's in good condition mechanically.'

In this book, designed to accompany, and in many ways to complement, the television series of the same title, I have tried to fit the themes touched on in the programmes into a socio-historical framework. But the factors involved are complicated, involving a triple relationship between the driver, the vehicle and the circumstances in which he or she is driving – which includes, but is not confined to, the roads and their furniture which disfigures them, helpless bystanders, the other occupants of this or another vehicle and those walking or cycling on or beside the road.

I have had to be selective and I've taken a lot for granted. In particular, I've paid relatively less attention to the cars and the roads, not only because of the content of the series, but also because readers will already be familiar with a great many of the facts and arguments involved, and instead I have tried to explore the outer reaches of the subject, social, medical, psychological, industrial and political. Also, full details of the books mentioned in the text can be found in the Select Bibliography on page 181.)

It would have been only too easy for me to fill the pages of this book with descriptions, more or less gory and affecting, of individual accidents. This I am unwilling to do, first because of a naïve squeamishness but also because of the 'pornography of violence' implicit in reading about – or, still more, seeing on the screen – such scenes. I have therefore kept actual crash examples to the minimum, at the risk of seeming rather cold-blooded about them. I prefer to be accused of bloodlessness, even of heartlessness, than indulgence in gory details.

I have also tried not to bandy around too many statistics. This is not only because they tend to be confusing, but also because they are even more unreliable when it comes to evaluating accidents than in most other instances. While road deaths are universally reported and therefore the figures can be used on a comparative basis, those for injuries are unreliable. First, and in notable contrast with air crashes, no one reports near misses, they merely talk about them afterwards, and many minor injuries go unreported – although I suspect that a higher proportion are reported now than was the case a generation ago, a phenomenon which has distorted the trend lines for other crimes, like rape.

More serious injuries are categorized haphazardly. As the British Medical Association told a House of Commons Committee in 1983, 'Only one in four casualties classified as seriously injured are, in fact, seriously injured, and many of those classified as slightly injured are, in fact, seriously injured. The existing [police] description of "seriously injured" covers everything from a broken finger to total paralysis and death occurring more than thirty days after an accident.' And, as John Adams points out, 'The number of injuries that get recorded relates to the number of people you have recording them. Below a certain threshold, some accidents are simply not worth reporting but that threshold can move up and down depending on how preoccupied the police are with other problems going on on their patch. For example, if they have more important things to do, then road accidents will be ignored and officially the roads may become safer.'

Finally, I feel that I should reveal my own driving record and my own attitude to safety, both of which must, inevitably, colour a book on so emotive a subject. Let me start by affirming that I'm not an expert and by no means an ideal driver. I'm aware of my sins, so I'm not liable to preach at my audience – and thus, I feel more suitable than more pious, though more expert, authors.

I learnt to drive in 1950–51 and passed my test at my second try. (I bumped into another car at my first attempt.) During the 1960s and 1970s I wrote about motoring and the motor industry for *The Economist* and the *Sunday Times* and was able through my work to drive a wide variety of cars and to learn a little about the thought processes of those involved in the manufacture and sales of cars and of the journalists who wrote about them. In all I must have driven up to 500,000 miles and during the past forty-six years I have, inevitably, been involved in a number of accidents – none, thank God, causing serious injury to me or anyone else. Typically, they were due to a multiplicity of causes: the unreliability of the brakes of an old car; my tiredness; an incautious cyclist swerving across my path. Of course I believe that I am a safe driver (don't we all?) but I am also aware that I habitually break speed limits, believing that I can judge, better than the authorities, the speed appropriate to the conditions of the road, my car and my physical state. I am also subject to fits of what can only be described as an endemic and impartial road irritation, covering everyone else on the road, whether they be drivers of other vehicles, motorcyclists, pedal cyclists or pedestrians.

Whatever this may say about me as a driver – and as a person – I feel it makes me a suitable person to write about the subject since I do so as an honest sinner, and in a spirit chastened by decades of continual reminders from my nearest and dearest that they don't think much of my driving skills (and even less of my attitudes). I am fully aware of my sins, past and present, and in my defence I can only remind the reader of the reproach made to Evelyn Waugh: how, his friends asked, could he be so awful a person when he was a devout Roman Catholic? Ah, replied Waugh, just think how awful I would be if I weren't a Christian. So it is with me. My potential danger as a driver is, I hope and believe, considerably diluted by my continuing awareness of my faults.

None the less, my experience as a driver, journalist and author leaves me angry at the many ways in which the car industry, governments and public opinion have played down the subject of road safety over the past century, and with a feeling that, despite the enormous advances in safety that I have witnessed over the past forty years, there is still more to be done. Yet today, and increasingly, we take precautions that were unheard of when I started driving. We 'belt up', we do not drive after having consumed more than a minimal quantity of alcohol. We drive on roads far less dangerous than in pre-motorway days and in cars far less likely to injure their occupants in the case of a crash than was the case even two decades ago. This book is written in the knowledge that things have improved, but could still be a lot better.

List of Interviewees

John Adams, Professor of Geography, University College, London, England

Dr Jeffrey Augenstein, Professor of Surgery at the University of Miami School of Medicine and trauma surgeon at the Rider Trauma Centre, part of Jackson Memorial Hospital in Miami, Florida, USA

Dr Howard Baderman, the first accident and emergency consultant in Britain

Faris Bandak, researcher into biomechanics, US Department of Transport

Dr Anthony Bleetman, consultant surgeon, Accident and Emergency, Heartlands Hospital, Birmingham, England

Byron Bloch, accident investigator

Dr Burgess, consultant orthopaedic surgeon, Cowley Shock Trauma Hospital, Baltimore, USA

Baroness (Barbara) Castle of Blackburn, former Minister of Transport

Jeff Crandall, automobile safety laboratory at the University of Virginia, studying impact biomechanics

Csaba Csere, editor-in-chief, *Car & Driver*

Dr Bob Davis, chairman of the Road Danger Reduction Forum

PC Mike Doyle, Accident Investigation Unit, West Midlands Police, England

Leonard Evans, principal research scientist, General Motors' Research and Development Center, Michigan, USA

Rex Grogan, tyre specialist

Dr Bob Gunther, psychologist, Rehabilitation Institute of Michigan, Detroit Medical Center, USA

Dave Holls, former senior designer, General Motors

Heinz Hubner, Director of Police, Berlin, Germany

Robert Jones, traffic homicide investigator, Dade County, Miami, USA

Ben Kelly, former senior official with National Highways Administration and later deputy director of Insurance Institute for Highway Safety, California, USA

Conrad King, psychologist

Charlie Komannoff, pedestrian activist

Jerry Kossar, project manager, Research Safety Vehicle, California, USA

9

Lord Lucas of Chilworth, former car salesman

Daniel McCarthy, road safety officer, Exeter, Devon, England

Professor Murray Mackay, Birmingham University, Britain's first automobile accident investigator

Robert McNamara, former President, Ford Motor Co, later US Secretary of Defense and President of the World Bank

Ralph Nader, safety campaigner

Bernhard Potter, editor, *Die Tageszeitung*, Berlin, Germany

Professor Hartmut Rau, accident expert

Siamack Salari, researcher, J. Walter Thompson, London, England

Dr Stefan Schmidt, doctor in Accident and Emergency, Berlin, Germany

David Silcock, transport consultant

Dr Alison Smiley, Human Factors North Inc., Toronto, Canada

John Stapp, safety campaigner

Dr Steve Stradling, psychologist, Driver Behaviour Research Group, Manchester University, England

John Telnack, Vice-president of Design at Ford Motor Co.

Charles Terlizzi, co-ordinator for Maryland of the National Motorists' Association, USA

Jose Miguel Trigoso, head of PRP, the official Portuguese road safety organization

Dr Pat Waller, director, University of Michigan Transportation Research Institute, USA

Malcolm Westwood, fire-fighter, West Midlands Fire Brigade, England

John Whitelegg, Professor of Environmental Studies, John Moores University, Liverpool, England

Gerald Wilde, Professor of Psychology, Queens University, Kingston, Ontario, Canada

Larry Zeitlin, psychologist, City University of New York

YESTERDAY

1

Transports of Delight

After the first road fatality in Britain in 1896 the coroner said, 'This must never happen again.' But it has, nearly twenty-five million times world-wide since then. Over 1.5 million crashes have happened in the US alone, where the first occurred on 13 September 1899. A certain Mr H. H. Bliss stepped off his trolley-car after a journey into New York City. At that point a Mr A. Smith, driving a new electric cab, tried to overtake the trolley-car. Mr Bliss stepped into his path – and into history as the first automobile fatality in the USA.

The history of our relationship with the private car includes many themes familiar to any student of the history of the twentieth century. Cars have became cult objects, worshipped in music and film. They have been seen as a status symbol, symbolizing the control we delude ourselves we can exercise over our environment from within a mobile capsule, and the capacity to express our own individuality – feelings directly opposed to the use of public transport. More positively, over the past half-century the car has become a symbol of democracy, of individual freedom, of people's rights to move as they wish. Nowhere has this been more the case than in the United States, historically a restless, mobile society, its national impatience summed up in the phrase 'Let's get moving.'

Behind all these psychological considerations lies one inescapable fact: the private car is an extraordinarily convenient way of getting about. It symbolizes, above all, the increasing freedom enjoyed by the mass of the population of the industrialized world. But the dangers, the problems, the tensions between the desire for freedom and the need to control its manifestations are bound to multiply in line with the numbers who enjoy the freedom: democratization has its costs as goods and services previously available only to a small wealthy élite have become available to all. More recently, the car has become *par excellence* the symbol of the 'me' society. And as John Cohen, remarks, in *Causes and Prevention of Motor Accidents*,

'One might as well say that "a man lives as he drives" . . . But the correlation between living and driving may be more complex and subtle than that epigram suggests. Driving may bring out elements which are normally concealed or suppressed in out-of-the-car behaviour.'

But all this is relatively recent. We tend to forget how far the car was the prerogative of an élite, not just in Britain but everywhere outside the United States until well after 1945. Until 1914 car owners were found almost exclusively among the rich and powerful (and their chauffeurs who were, socially, simply their instruments), and in Britain, at least, until 1939 there was a powerful undertone of class superiority in owning and driving a car, despite the spread between the wars of more popular motoring. Before 1939 the relative lack of traffic meant that the driver had a certain amount of freedom on the roads – the only exception being the decidedly down-market hordes caught in bank holiday traffic jams on their journeys to and from the coast.

Even before 1945, the increase in motoring had brought about a socio-political-judicial revolution: it was the first time that the car-owning and driving classes had ever thought of the government, the state, and in particular its instruments, the police and the judiciary, as not being 'on their side', ready to help them in any little difficulties they might encounter, but controlling them and going so far even as to charge them with their misdemeanours on the roads. And not in their tens or hundreds, but in their hundreds of thousands. They fought any extension of 'social' control over their motoring activities with what they felt was righteous indignation, fuelled by the idea, real or imagined, that they were fighting a more general battle for individual rights against an unjustifiably encroaching state. Less sympathetic observers came to the conclusion that they were acting purely on behalf of a selfish, and indeed dangerous, class. It is almost as though the authorities were imposing on the public the sort of view of human life associated with Thomas Hobbes, the seventeenth-century English philosopher, that without strict restraints life would inevitably be 'nasty, brutish and short'.

Reading about early drivers takes one back to the world of Mr Toad, in Kenneth Grahame's *The Wind in the Willows*, who represented precisely the type of loud-mouthed, anti-social, exhibitionist motorist associated with the Edwardian *nouveaux riches*. It may seem unbelievable to today's readers, but Toad is not a fictional exaggeration, he is a composite portrait of contemporary motoring attitudes. Until 1914, motorists were few, rich and unpopular. Envy played a part in their unpopularity but more important was their lack of concern for the lives of pedestrians or anyone else in their often erratic path. A friend recalled none other than the Hon. Charles Rolls, joint founder of Rolls-Royce, boasting of the terror he caused when thundering through an otherwise peaceful countryside, how 'I saw some old ladies jump the wall of a churchyard. We passed a field with farm labourers working near the edge of the road; the whole company ran away at full speed across the big field.' According to Richard Sutton in *Motor Mania*, an Edwardian advertisement promoted De Dion's luxurious cars by showing the terror caused by a driver 'running over two terrified pigs and narrowly missing a horse-drawn cart (significantly driven by a pale-faced Eastern immigrant, rather than a Westerner), the horse rearing up in terror'.

This arrogance produced reaction: as early as 1905, the death of a young child under the wheels of a car belonging to Hildebrand Harmsworth, a member of the newspaper family, became a *cause célèbre* and, in consequence, even *The Times* condemned the minority of reckless drivers. Nevertheless, the sheer exhilaration of fast driving, combined with a typical scorn for 'lesser breeds', prevented any serious protest. As early as 1911, though, *The Economist* posed the fundamental question: 'Is the loss of comfort or convenience, and the positive annoyance suffered by the public, compensated for by the intensity of the pleasure obtained by a comparative handful of individuals?' A year later it reflected on how it was 'amazing that in a civilized community . . . the pursuit of pleasure in our streets and high roads should be allowed to cause . . . this enormous loss of life, limb and property'.

But the bravado – or madness, as we might now see it – continued right through the inter-war years. Perhaps the most extraordinary example was the Hundred Mile An Hour Club, consisting exclusively of drivers who had achieved 'the ton' driving down Park Lane in London's West End, generally in the early hours of the morning. Sutton records one veteran enthusiast, Red Daniells, telling of the 'rather marvellous night' when seven or eight young 'scorchers' – as these chaps were called – descended on to the Embankment where eight of them 'roared along both sides of the road. Suddenly a young policeman stepped out to stop us. Some of us went on the pavement to avoid him, others went up Sloane Street, some went over the bridge and down the pie-stall straight and some went straight on. With us all disseminated all he could do was shout after us.'

These bright young things found supporters even among their elders and betters. At one meeting of the Pedestrians' Association, then a powerful organization,* the well-known author Rose Macaulay ridiculed the idea that it was important *not* to rush into legislation 'but that people must be educated to get out of the way more quickly! That very day a man who had killed two women was acquitted with honour at the Old Bailey, and,

---

*A meeting in protest at road accidents in November 1933 attracted representatives from dozens of other organizations, ranging from trade unions to the National Institute of Industrial Psychology.

according to the newspapers, the judge said to him *kindly*, "Do you think you had better go on driving when you cannot see?" '

The then prevalence of the court's attitude lent a peculiar intensity and bitterness to the attempts made in Britain in the late 1920s and 1930s to impose some form of control over cars and their drivers, since these depended on the consent of the powerful people involved.

It seemed even difficult to decide what constituted dangerous driving. The original definition was based on that applied to horse-drawn traffic in the Highways Act of 1835, which made it an offence to drive 'recklessly, negligently or furiously'. But how could this be applied to motorists? As William Plowden points out in *The Motor Car & Politics 1896–1970*, 'After many thousands of years of the horse, anyone could recognize when a horse was travelling at a normal pace and when it was going too fast. The signs of "fury" were equally clear: the foam and sweat of the horse, the shouts and gestures of its driver.' With cars there was no such clear-cut evidence. Hence, the reliance over the years on speed limits. Speed limits were a 'least worst' solution to the insoluble problem of definition, and they created one of the major problems that face any attempt to impose legal restrictions on drivers: their unenforceability. Plowden quotes an early objector, Henry Norman, MP, who thundered that speed limits were unenforceable because they were unjust 'against the good sense and conscience of a large part of the community'. They were, indeed, unenforceable: in 1933 a Royal Commission found that during a whole year in half the counties in Britain there had been no prosecutions at all for speeding.

The Commission put the dilemma with admirable succinctness: 'Public opinion may be relied upon to support the enforcement of a law against reckless, negligent or dangerous driving, which is necessarily a menace to all other users of the roads. But the enforcement of a maximum speed limit does not command the same unanimous support and sympathy,' although it had one perhaps surprising supporter. According to a leading diplomat, Sir Nevile Henderson, George V used to comment on the annual accident figures 'in his usual emphatic manner'. 'No cars', he asserted, 'should ever be allowed to be driven at a speed of over thirty miles an hour.'

In Britain the realization that cars were dangerous weapons became ever more widespread at the end of the 1920s. The figures tell the story: from 4886 deaths in 1926, fatalities rose remorselessly, year by year, to 5300 in 1927 and 6100 a year later, all at a time when, in theory, the country was covered by a blanket 20 m.p.h. speed limit. As the death rate rose, when there were only a million cars in use, Britain's motorists were finally subjected to some form of discipline.

But it took a long and hard-fought battle to impose some order on the chaos. The opposition to any such measures was ferocious. In 1927, for instance, Lord Montagu objected thunderously to proposals that private cars might be restricted in towns. Plowden quotes him: 'But shall we ever stand such a denial of individual liberty? If I am right in my opinion that the right to use the road, that wonderful emblem of liberty, is deeply engraved in our history and character, such action will meet with the most stubborn opposition. More street space and more road space will have to be provided whatever be the plan for it or the cost of it' – a cry that echoed through the public arena for another fifty years.

Another theme, the economic importance of the industry, was noted by Lord Cecil of Chelwood, the long-serving president of the Pedestrians' Association. When he introduced a Road Vehicles Regulation Bill, 'motor manufacturers, automobile clubs, automobile associations, one after another, came in a kind of procession all saying pretty much the same thing . . . : "Whatever you do, don't touch the motor trade . . . It is far more important that we should make our money than that people should be safe."' Sixty years later, Dr Bob Gunther, of the Rehabilitation Institute of Michigan, reiterates the theme: 'There is a huge industry riding in the back seat of the automotive industry. It consists of the insurance companies, the health-care industry and the automotive-repair industry, which is massive. Those industries exist because the motor vehicle is so dangerous, because of the carnage that results from its everyday use.'

In 1934, drivers were subjected to a number of elementary disciplines, summed up for an older generation of motorists in the 'Belisha beacons', the warning lights at pedestrian crossings named after Leslie Hore-Belisha, the then Minister of Transport. These, like other improvements, were due rather to his predecessor, Oliver Stanley, one of the few Ministers of Transport to make a real impression in a post which, as in the United States, has usually acted as a short-term staging post for politicians on their way up – or, more usually, down. (Perhaps the most distinguished exception in Britain is Barbara Castle, the subject of Chapter 4.)

Stanley's analysis started from the recognition that during 1933 the public had been clamouring for action. He concluded that 'there is no single cause to which accidents can be exclusively or indeed predominantly attributed', a view in sharp contrast with the tendency at the time to blame the driver, and which led him to urge co-ordinated action from police, government, courts, road-users and highway authorities. He proposed speed limits, compulsory insurance, pedestrian crossings, the prohibition of inefficient bicycle reflectors and widespread propaganda to back it all up. It was the boldness and cohesion of his programme that saw it through. As Plowden puts it: 'Never before had a government so deliberately resolved that, however the motorists might protest, their protests should be disregarded in the interests of public safety.' To modern eyes these regulations seemed minimal – and driving tests were only imposed on new motorists from 1934.

The measures had some positive effects. By 1939 road deaths had risen to 8,272 per year, but the rate had fallen dramatically since, by the outbreak of war, there were twice as many cars on the road as at the start of the decade. Nevertheless in 1933 the blame for crashes was placed on the private car and the motorcycle for three in every five accidents, a proportion that had increased by 1938 to four in five. However, the reluctance of the professional middle classes in convicting their own kind showed up in the way magistrates avoided the endorsement or suspension of licences, mandatory for speeding or careless driving: Plowden tells of one instance when a driver was let off although he had been speeding and was uninsured because he 'had done special radiological work for the King when he was indisposed recently'.

Unfortunately, this flurry of activity also enshrined a heresy that poisoned attempts to reduce the toll on the roads for thirty years or more: it was the idea that crashes were caused solely by the driver of the car – the 'nut behind the wheel'. The motoring community was fully aware that this was by no means the whole story. As veteran motorist Ronald Barker explained to Richard Sutton in *Motor Mania*: 'It wasn't speed that was at the heart of bad driving, it was lack of control.' This, as Sutton goes on to say, 'was due to driver ineptitude, poor grip, variable road surfaces and brakes operating on only the rear wheels' – four-wheel brakes were still unusual in the 1930s except on the newest cars. Barker remembers, above all, the sheer inconsistency of the road surfaces: 'There was little more alarming to the driver than a change from tarmac to gravel or shingle, especially at night when you really couldn't see it coming.' Nevertheless, in 1937 the Alness Committee echoed the American doctrine that improvement could come only from the '3 Es', Engineering, Education, Enforcement.

Over-concentration on the driver never made much sense. As Ralph Nader was to point out thirty years later (in *Unsafe at Any Speed*): 'Vehicle deficiencies are more important to correct than human inadequacies simply because they are easier to analyse and to remedy.'

In the United States the first two conferences on road safety, called by Herbert Hoover, then Secretary of Commerce, in 1924 and 1926, set a pattern that prevailed for nearly forty years. The emphasis was decidedly on the 'three Es', which had been established (by the Safety First League of Boston) some ten years earlier. Needless to say, the last two referred purely to the driver while engineering was held to refer only to the road and not, curiously, to the vehicle. The emphasis was on 'making guilt work' as far as the driver was concerned. Typical of many exhortations was that published in *Motor Age* in 1916: 'Statistics prove that 90 per cent of accidents contain at least an element of contributory negligence', an attitude reinforced nine years later in *Collier's*, then an immensely influential magazine: 'Automobiles are now nearly fool-proof. Streets are not, and some drivers are fools.'

When the dangers of driving became increasingly apparent in the 1930s Henry Ford said, 'Safety is baloney, the driver is the problem', which he, his rivals and successors repeated until the 1980s. (A modern commentary on this delusion comes from Dr Pat Waller of the Michigan Transportation Research Institute, who 'heard an eminent human-factors psychologist refer to that nut behind the wheel as the one who keeps the vehicle engineer and the highway engineer out of prison'.)

One of the best illustrations of the way drivers were automatically blamed for accidents came in a sensational and highly influential article, 'And Sudden Death' by J. C. Furnas, published by *Reader's Digest* in 1935.* The article, inspired by an accident witnessed by the magazine's founder De Witt Wallace, was preceded by a warning that it might 'nauseate some readers'. Even today it makes strong reading. It was based on the theme that 'What is needed is a vivid and *sustained* realization that every time you step on the throttle death gets in beside you, hopefully waiting for its chance. The single horrible accident you may have witnessed is no isolated horror.' The author is unsparing of his readers:

> Minor details would include the raw ends of bones protruding
> through flesh in compound fractures and the dark red, oozing
> surfaces where clothes and skin were flayed off at once. Ghosts could
> be put to a useful purpose, every bad stretch of road in the United
> States would greet the oncoming motorist with groans and screams
> and the educational spectacle of ten or a dozen corpses, all sizes,
> sexes and ages, lying horribly still on the bloody grass.

Such prose was understandable at a time when 'there have been as many as 27 fatalities in one summer month' on a single stretch of three-lane road, the Astor Flats on the Albany Post Road in upstate New York. But blame was fixed on the driver – even after the author had singled out the appalling injuries caused by flying glass, when safety glass was not in universal use, and by the 'projectiles' in the shape of projecting knobs in the car itself. The magazine offered cheap reprints of the article because it was convinced that 'widespread reading of this article will help curb reckless driving'. There was no question of calling for less lethal cars.

The article was, indeed, enormously influential. In the words of Paul Hoffman of Studebaker, one of the few executives in the industry interested in safety, it provided 'the greatest single impetus to the [highway safety] program'. It was 'a spark that touched off a tremendous explosion of public interest and concern'. But it did not address the subject of the cars

---

*An indication of its importance is that it was one of the rare articles that the magazine did not even pretend had previously been published elsewhere.

themselves. As Joel Eastman points out in *Styling v. Safety, the American Automobile Industry and the Development of Automotive Safety*, its purpose 'was not to advocate safer design of automobile interiors – and this alternative was not even mentioned – but rather to frighten people into driving safely so that accidents would not occur in the first place'.

Opponents of the industry's view that drivers – and inadequate highways – were at fault were few and far between. One author cried in the wilderness: in a book published in 1941, Arthur W. Stevens pointed out that inexorably mounting accident statistics proved the futility of the policy based on the three Es: 'Instead of placing the 131,000,000 people of this country in one classroom it would be more practical to teach a couple of hundred top executives in the industry how to design safer automobiles.' But he didn't stand a chance against a world influenced by, for example, a 1940s Warner Brothers cartoon of a driver sprouting horns and mowing down pedestrians.

It helped the industry that the law developed in such a way that in cases of death or injury it was the driver of the car who was assumed to be at fault, guilty of one of a group of vague offences, like 'careless' or 'reckless' driving. As the safety campaigner Ralph Nader put it in *Unsafe at Any Speed*, 'No distinction is drawn between the behaviour of the driver and the behaviour of the vehicle. Insofar as the law is violated, they are one. Thus the driver is heir to all the dangers created by the automobile designers, not only in terms of his bodily exposure but also in terms of legal exposure.' A natural consequence was a general failure, not confined to the United States, to investigate accidents in any depth since the driver was assumed to be at fault.

This happy state of affairs – so far as the industry was concerned – continued for another twenty years after 1945, even though the authorities had to admit that the Educational E had proved pretty futile. The 1948 edition of the British government's *Social Survey* concluded that 'the public as a whole was immune to warnings about danger on the roads, and that neither the temperament nor the behaviour of the individual was much affected by visual propaganda'. (I remember a poster of about the same date with the caption Keep Death off the Road accompanying a photograph of a stricken widow. In our family it became a black joke and, indeed, one unfortunate friend was referred to as 'Keep Death off the Road'.) In the mid-1960s this age of relative innocence, of wonder and worship at the glory of the motor car, came to a sudden end.

2

Highway to Safety
I: Unsafe at Any Speed

On 9 March 1966 I was in Detroit reporting on the state of the US motor industry for *The Economist*. Naturally I called on the *New York Times* bureau chief, Walter Rugaber. Earlier that day the crusading lawyer, safety campaigner and author Ralph Nader had revealed that he had been followed by private detectives. They had done a thorough job of investigating his background, his sex life and his political attitudes – he is of Lebanese origin and the detectives may have hoped to find an anti-Semitic streak in him. They had even tried to set him up as a shoplifter. Rugaber and I spent the whole of dinner trying to figure out who was responsible. Certainly Nader did not lack enemies in Detroit: his book, *Unsafe at Any Speed*, published the previous December and a damning indictment of the automobile industry and its influence, had become a best-seller.

Earlier that day both Ford and Chrysler had publicly denied employing the gumshoes and it seemed to both Rugaber and myself – as to every other observer at the time – inconceivable that that monument of respectability, General Motors (GM), could have been responsible. After dinner, we returned to Rugaber's office, only to find that news agencies were reporting that GM had been forced to admit employing the detectives.

I tell this story, not in any vainglorious attempt to point out that I Was There, but to illustrate the fact that, as late as 1966, it was simply unthinkable that GM could behave in such a silly, shoddy fashion. Twelve years earlier, journalists and other cynics had scoffed at the statement by Charlie Wilson, GM's chairman who became Eisenhower's Secretary of Defence that 'what's good for GM is good for the United States'* but they accepted that it was something of a truism. GM had bolstered its reputation with corporate advertising campaigns under the banner 'General Motors is People' – describing itself on occasion as 'Originator' and 'Perfectionist' –

---

*Although he went on to say, 'What's good for the United States is good for GM.'

21

and before Nader's arrival its claims to be acting as a 'worthy keeper of the people's trust' had gone largely unchallenged.

That March night GM lost its previously spotless reputation. The admission marked the sudden end of a period in which, as the veteran researcher (and former senior official with the National Highways Administration) Ben Kelly puts it, the manufacturers could adopt 'a very dismissive attitude toward the public in matters of automotive safety'. Until then they had asserted that 'first of all, if you get into an accident and somebody's hurt it's your fault, second of all, you're really not smart enough to understand the engineering and technological issues involved in making cars safe; and third of all, and the most serious, they have withheld needed motor vehicle safety information from people because they claimed they didn't want to alarm them – but, in fact, because they didn't want to admit that the car was defective. Under the guise of not wanting to frighten people they have withheld critically needed safety information from people for decades and that's caused a lot of death and injury.'

From that March night on, the automobile industry, previously the symbol of American technical and economic superiority, became the emblem of a callous and systematic disregard for human life. The date marked the beginning of consumerism, the organized revolt of those who felt themselves helpless in the face of the massive businesses that supplied the public with goods and services, and it made a decisive launch pad for the career of Ralph Nader, a figure unique in the world for his influence and dedication* – and the only consumer activist ever to grace the front cover of *Time* magazine.

The incident, coming so soon after Nader's book, triggered a quarter-century of conflict between an industry that had previously called all the shots, but was now on the defensive, and assorted safety experts, politicians and journalists led by Ralph Nader and 'Nader's Raiders', the small group of supporters he had assembled. In retrospect, what was surprising was not the industry's eventual acceptance of its responsibility for safety on the road so much as the length of time it took to call it to account.

In the twenty years after 1945, the motor-car, and everything associated with it, was the most glamorous growth industry, comparable to personal computers in the 1980s but on a far larger scale. During that period the number of cars registered in the United States rose nearly three-fold from 31 million to 89 million, far outstripping the rise in population, while car owners drove ever further, their mileage increasing three and a half times in the same period. As Dave Holls, a retired Cadillac designer and GM employee, points out, the automobile became the centre of the nation's

---

*Thirty-one books have been written about him, including *Ralph Nader, Will You Marry Me?* by an obsessed spiritualist.

whole life: 'It created suburban life because now you were mobile. Your house now had a carport, which was designed with the house. You went to drive-in theatres, drive-in restaurants, everything was centred around that car. Your vehicle was your personal prestige put on the line when you went to these places, so the more dramatic and the more beautiful your car was, the more you were proud to bring it to these various places that were designed around the automobile.'

The automotive industry's power was immense: one business in six was connected with it and one worker in seven was employed, directly or indirectly, in producing, supplying, servicing, financing or transporting automobiles or their parts. In the – admittedly jaundiced – view of Ralph Nader, this turned the United States into the industrial equivalent of a 'one-crop economy': a sort of 'motor republic' similar to the banana republics of Central America, helplessly in the grip of the corporations that dominated their economic life. And within the industry by far the dominant influence was General Motors, far and away the largest company in the country, with over half of the market. Right through the 1950s Ford was financially convalescent, having been virtually bankrupt in 1945, and Chrysler not an important factor in the market. 'If Chevvy* dropped its prices $25 it would bankrupt Chrysler' went the saying, 'and if the price dropped $50 it would bankrupt Ford.'

Perhaps the most nefarious example of GM's power emerged only in the 1970s through a Senate investigation. This revealed that it had headed a group of major companies that had bought and then shut down the light rail systems used for mass transit in Los Angeles, replacing it partially and inadequately, with buses, nine out of ten of which were made by GM. The 1964 riots in the Watts section of Los Angeles were directly traceable to the inhabitants' inability to get to work by public transport.

The manufacturers were at the heart of a web of almost equally influential businesses, most importantly component suppliers and dealers whose profits were boosted by the fragility of many of the cars' components. Ben Kelly remembers going on a tour of a warehouse with Henry Ford II. Pointing to 'rows and rows and rows of fenders and door panels, Ford started to muse that these were so delicate that we had to pay a tremendous amount to ship them and they got damaged all the time when they were being shipped from here to the dealers. It didn't strike me until much later that what he was saying was that these parts were so delicate and so expensive that they were made to be damaged and made to be replaced and

---

*Chevrolet was only one, albeit the largest, of GM's five marques. Its power was summed up in the words of a famous song:
    'I ain't' a' goin' to go to Heaven in a Ford V-8
    'Cos the Lord got shares in Chevrolet.'

made to increase profits for the car company.'

The 1950s which conformed an era with the prevailing ethos: the years after McCarthyism were not a time when radical challenges were frequent or effective. Within business it was the heyday of the Organization Man, a type first defined in William Whyte's book published in 1957 in which an employee's loyalty to the corporation was paramount – and there was no corporation that commanded greater automatic loyalty among its executives than GM. Throughout the post-war era the industry's motto was 'we hire the engineers out of the universities and teach them the industry way' for GM was the archetype of an enclosed universe, its inhabitants insulated from the world outside.

In this context it was not surprising that Howard K. Gandelot, the engineer in charge of GM's safety efforts, such as they were, was a former test driver. Like many of his fellows he was convinced, as Joel Eastman puts it, that: 'Accidents were an act of God and it was of little use to design with this possibility [of a crash] in mind.' Perhaps the best illustration of the industry's fatalistic attitude towards safety comes in a story told by Dave Holls of a visit to Cadillac's ad agency: 'One time I remember we went over there and they were showing the new cars for the next year and I look, and here is a hearse going into a cemetery, and the Cadillac script underneath the hearse said "Eventually, why not now?"'

While the 'nut behind the wheel' theory still strongly prevailed, there was also growing opinion that contributing factors in the causes of road crashes should be considered. Gandelot's colleague, Kenneth A. Stonex, who had worked for GM for thirty years and was the chief spokesman on the subject of car safety, clearly believed that his principal job was to support the campaign to rebuild the country's major road system, seen throughout the industry as the key to improving safety on the roads; for, in Nader's words, it was 'the leading cause of death among people between the age of five and thirty and the fourth leading cause of death in this country. Car accidents account for over one-third of people hospitalized by injuries in the nation; they are the leading cause of injury to eyes and ears and cause over twenty-five per cent of partial and complete paralysis due to injury.' The natural response was to build an enormous and ever-expanding network of motorways (freeways in the USA), initiated by President Eisenhower, who in 1919 as a young officer had commanded a convoy of lorries that crossed the country in a dramatic demonstration to show that virtually all the country's roads were unfit for motors.

The dangers inside the cars were real enough too. The veteran campaigner Byron Bloch decribes the attitude of 1950s motorists. Pointing to a 1956 Buick made by General Motors, typical of the cars of the fifties, he says: 'My family owned one of these. It has these lethal design features in it. These were unknown killers at the time. The rigid steering column could harpoon you in the chest, would impale the driver. The knife-like edges of the steering wheel would cut into your chest, your neck and your face. The key to the ignition switch was right in front of your knee and would fracture and shatter your kneecap in a frontal crash. The instrument panel had all kinds of knobs and edges and protrusions that would also be lethal in a crash. The so-called padded instrument panel was really a token effort towards safety in the fifties and yet beneath the thin pad you had the rigid metal edge that itself could be lethal. You have the rigid spike of a rear-view mirror attachment that would fracture your skull as you went forward in the frontal accident. The instrument panel also had a glove-box door that would often pop open and had a guillotine edge that would slice into and decapitate a small child in a frontal accident. All of these features were found in just about all the cars of the fifties. These were secret defects, secret hazards. The public had no idea that these killers were hiding in their car ready to impale them, slice into them, decapitate them, kill them in a frontal crash.'

But even Bloch 'loved the fifties. I loved my friends, I loved the music and I loved the cars of the fifties, they were so exciting to me. I would sneak into the car dealerships every fall just to get the first glimpse of the new models. I would study meticulously the details of the instrument panel, the grille, the tail-lights, every curve and contour of these glamorous, exciting cars. To me it was the excitement of all time to have these beautiful, beautiful cars that I could see, that I could touch, that I could smell, that I could feel, that I could drive. As a teenager growing up in Chicago these cars meant everything to me. It was an inspiration to see every year the new cars when they would come out, but I especially remember the Motoramas of the 1950s.' As John Telnack, a senior designer at Ford, remembers them, the Motoramas 'were very extravagant. They had, you know, great music, a lot of dancing girls. I can remember some of the presentations where they had concept cars on platforms that would be lifted and spun around and come out right in front of the audience and almost dropped in your lap, they were just great displays and caused a lot of excitement.'

The Motoramas were designed to draw attention to the great event in the industry's – and the nation's – year: the annual model change. This was no novelty – the idea went back to the inter-war years – but it reached its zenith in the 1950s. The process, which involved every detail of the cars' exterior styling – though not their mechanical components – was called 'dynamic obsolescence' by Harley Earl, GM's all-powerful head of styling. His subordinate, William Mitchell, the chief stylist, presided over a staff of 1400 styling specialists. The rationale behind these continually changing gimmicks was epitomized in a Buick ad: 'You don't really need these, but how can you resist them?'

It was the dream of many American youngsters to be part of this most glamorous of shows. As Dave Holls says: 'You know, to be a stylist at GM in that era I always thought was the best job in the world, where you could have so much fun and get paid for it.'

In theory the Great American Public disapproved of the rapid rate of change – a 1958 poll showed that it was opposed by 50 per cent of the population and approved by only 38 per cent – but in reality car buyers voted with their wallets for the latest model. Cars like those from Volkswagen, which preached a different message (that is, of the car as a functional object rather than a status symbol), occupied only a marginal place in the market.

The mounting of an effective campaign against this combination of power, glamour and lifestyle, the *Zeitgeist* of the time, seemed a hopeless task. The consumer had no power base, no elected representatives, their constituency was unorganized, and the prevailing view of the American people continued to be that the 'nut behind the wheel' was responsible for all the accidents not caused by bad roads. The press was in no position to counterbalance the industry's influence. It was dominated by small papers largely dependent on advertising by the manufacturers, and by the almost equally important dealers. Many motoring journalists were – and still are – what was described as 'two-hatters', who reported on the industry while at the same time selling car-related advertising. Even at the national level, *Reader's Digest*, which had not hesitated to attack the powerful tobacco industry and to reject its advertising, refused to tackle the iniquities of the automobile industry.

The structure of the American system of government was seemingly designed to shelter the automobile industry from surveillance. At the federal level, no independent agency was devoted to the problem. The remit of the Department of Commerce was to 'foster, promote and develop' commerce and industry. As its name implies, the Federal Highways Administration was dedicated to building roads and was largely dependent on state authorities, themselves peculiarly subject to local political pressure. The high-sounding President's Action Committee for Traffic Safety, was a farce: its first chairman, Harlow H. Curtice, was the then president of GM. In other words, the industry had either hijacked or neutered the few official organizations that might have alerted the American public to its sins. The low priority attached to safety can be shown by a simple statistic: in 1965 the Senate allocated over $300 million to help beautify the country's highway by removing thousands of billboards; the same act provided $5 million for a study on how to dispose of scrapped cars – and '$500,000 for a Commerce Department study of auto safety'.

Most of the responsibility for road safety had devolved downwards, to the administrations of individual states, not because they were likely to be more vigilant or effective but for precisely the opposite reasons. The only man to point this out was a maverick intellectual and future senator, Daniel Patrick Moynihan, then a political-science teacher: 'The typical bureau of motor vehicles is filled with deservedly ill-paid clerks and run by an assortment of genial "pols"* with utterly no training or interest in traffic safety except as it provides an opportunity to do small favours.'† Unsurprisingly, the contemporary files of the motor industry are full of glowing tributes to the administrators' work.

In the 1950s Moynihan produced by far the most sustained intellectual criticism of the industry. He attacked the basis on which accident statistics were judged and was prepared to take on even such supposedly public-spirited bodies as the National Safety Council. 'By emphasizing the individual's responsibility in automobile accidents,' he pointed out, 'the Safety Council shifts public attention from factors such as automobile design, which we can reasonably hope to control, to factors such as the temperament and behaviour of eighty million drivers, which are not susceptible to any form of consistent, overall control – certainly not by a bunch of slogans.'‡

The industry's influence was so great that the few reports on safety that did filter out from research studies, whether privately or publicly funded, did not name names and generally reported on vehicles as anonymous objects. The few exceptions, like Consumer Reports with their long-standing criticisms of many aspects of automobile design, could be ignored. 'No other consumer product,' wrote Nader, 'has enjoyed such immunity of specific criticism. The automobile, by brand name, stands as a sacred cow.'

Nader was writing after twenty years during which, as he pointed out, 'the gap between existing design and attainable safety has widened enormously'. Unfortunately, in his natural concern to present himself as the single most important influence on car safety this century, Nader tends to play down the way in which his predecessors had prepared the ground for the breakthrough he achieved in 1965–6. Nevertheless, that handful of dissident voices had not formed an effective lobby. In 1956 a spokesman for the National Safety Council admitted that 'past researches have been fragmentary, inconclusive and unco-ordinated', to which list he could have added 'under-funded and under-publicized'. Typical was the treatment of a distinguished inventor and academic, Professor James Ryan of the University of Minnesota. On a minuscule budget – $140,000 – he developed automatic seat-belts, greatly improved steering wheels and dashboards and, most importantly, hydraulic shock-absorbing bumpers. These, he proved, could prevent all but the most minor injuries in a crash

---

*Abbreviation for (generally corrupt) 'political appointees'.
†In Eastman, *Styling v. Safety*.
‡*Ibid.*

at up to 40 m.p.h. The industry merely jeered.

Fortunately other pioneers had a greater effect, and none more so than John Stapp. Like many other researchers, he remembers vividly the first car crash he ever witnessed, 'at 5 o'clock in the morning in December of 1936 when I was taking a bus ride to St Louis from the University of Texas at Austin, where I was a graduate student, to attend a research conference, and on that snowy morning this man in his pick-up truck had slammed into a power pole, skidding on the road. His car had one of these moveable windshield frames with little clamps to hold the main shield in place. He was thrown sideways into this protruding metal and it penetrated his temple – a huge man, I think he was a coal miner – and he was dead.'

Stapp, an Air Force officer, engineer and biophysicist, had been experimenting for years on human survival after crashes, first in the air. In 1947 he built a rocket sled and remembers that 'Between 1947 and 1970, with all the various devices, we accomplished over 5,000 human experiments without a single loss of life, without a single permanently disabling injury and without a single lawsuit.' His most dramatic experiment was when Stapp himself was shot in a rocket to the unbelievable speed of 632 m.p.h. Even today he remembers that 'it felt like hell but the ignition of those nine rockets, 45,000 pounds of thrust applied in just 70 thousandths of a second, was a surge forward and the effect was a dimming of vision, beginning of a black-out. With no windshield, but with a helmet and flying suit on the subject, sand grains in the air left little blisters on the shoulders through the clothing and there's immediate reversal in vision to brilliant brightness. Then it turned into a red-out and it was rather painful until we hit the water brakes and the congestion immediately diminished. But the red-out persisted for eight minutes after the sled was put on a stretcher. Looking up through a red haze, in about a minute or two I could see blue and all I had after that was uncontrolled double vision. I stayed in the hospital just two days under observation and by that time they were so aggravated they were glad to see me go!'

But his self-inflicted ordeal had a profound influence in that it showed the enormous forces the human body could survive if properly protected, and led to the cockpit design of the F-106 fighter, which never failed a single pilot. When the experiments were repeated to show their relevance to motor-cars, the industry didn't want to know. As Stapp says today, 'The car industry considered safety as something of a nuisance. General Motors gave a retired test driver, who took every thousandth car off the line and spun it around the track to prove that it worked, the job of safety chief of General Motors. An illustration of his approach to safety was that he said he had trained his children so that in view of an impending crash he'd yell, "Hands," and they'd put their hands on the back of the front seat or on the dash and that should save them. The attitude was more or less of disregard and contempt, and safety was a forbidden word in any advertising because they didn't want customers scared away by thinking that cars weren't safe.'

Yet Stapp's influence was both immediate and long-term. As he points out: 'Well before the seat-belt standards came into play, the industry quietly set their own standards through the Society of Automotive Engineers for 2,500-pound test locks on all the doors so that jettisoning of people out of cars during roll-overs and so on would be prevented.'

But it was his own example that had the greatest effect. To force the public to think about the safety of their cars, 'It took publicity and the publicity that that run [in the rocket sled] that I took got, including the cover story in *Time* magazine, put me on the trail of being invited to speak everywhere and to promote safety. I was a safety missionary.' This came naturally to a man both of whose parents had been missionaries. 'My gospel was safety and I can recall that when I was chief of the Air Medical Laboratory at Wright Field, in 1959 I travelled 175,000 miles and made 204 major speeches. I had innumerable press conferences and many times was called to Congress to meet with committees trying to put together safety laws and trying to justify and organize a Department of Transportation, and that came to pass in 1967.' Stapp's dramatic experiments and his annual safety conferences – attended by the young Ralph Nader – kept the spotlight on the subject, although he was becoming unpopular with his superiors; 'Unsafe At Any Rank', is the way he put it.

The cause of safety owes even more to a pathologist and engineer, Hugh de Haven. He had started his researches as a pilot in the First World War when he had witnessed a number of accidents and had himself suffered major injuries from the badly designed safety-belts of the period. He became convinced that engineers could not and would not make any improvements until doctors had collected data about survivability, and so investigated suicide attempts when people had leapt from skyscrapers and survived.

For the next forty years he persisted in his work, helped by a sympathetic police officer in Indiana and minuscule funds from the medical department of Cornell University, where he moved his pioneering Automobile Crash Injury Research Centre, of which he remained director until 1955 when he retired. The ACIR had another backer in the US Air Force, which had discovered during the Korean war that it was losing more men through car crashes than in combat. The Army confirmed this, and money was found through – of all bodies – the Armed Forces Epidemiological Board to fund a series of studies. Also, Liberty Mutual, a major insurance company, provided funds for a 'safety car', which received much attention – except from the automobile industry.

Early in 1955 the ACIR, by now also backed by the US Public Health Service, issued a crushing report on the newest cars, comparing those made between 1950 and 1954 with earlier post-war models: 'The contention that present day automobiles are "safer" in injury-producing accidents is not borne out by the facts.' The manufacturers responded by giving minimal sums to the ACIR and thus bought its silence – or, at least, prevented it from naming the vehicles it criticized – although in one report it pointed out that cars made by GM were twice as likely to have their doors torn off in an accident than those produced by Chrysler or Ford.

By 1961 the ACIR's successor, the Cornell Aeronautical Laboratory, had defined three general requirements for collision protection in a vehicle, which remain valid to this day: a sound outer shell, which would retain its structural integrity under impact; the elimination from the interior of the vehicle of sharp, hard projections or edges; and the fitting of passenger restraint systems. They found that the most obvious cause of unnecessary death and injury was the steering column, which accounted for one in five of the cases studied by Cornell's investigators, either when the driver was thrown forward into it or impaled on the steering column. But in the mid-1950s, when some manufacturers introduced a recessed steering wheel, the objective was clearly styling, not safety. As Murray Burnstine, an accident investigator from Harvard, commented at the time: 'In many cases they function only well enough to allow the motorist to die in the hospital instead of on the road.' When GM introduced 'a new windshield glass which nearly doubles occupant-penetration protection,' the corporation did not add the vital information that the improved protection merely doubled the speed at which it was effective from 12.5 to 24 m.p.h. without threatening the victim with a necklace of jagged glass.

Even more serious injuries were being caused by the instrument panel. As Hugh de Haven told a House of Representatives' sub-committee in 1959, for many years the manufacturers had been putting into automobiles 'an instrument panel that has the characteristics that are not too different, so far as the head and face are concerned, from a steel beam or an anvil'. They had been shamed already into putting padding on their panels – albeit as an optional extra – but the padding was too thin to be effective in serious accidents. And, as one specialist said flatly, 'GM's instrument panels are the most dangerous in the world'. Typically, Hunter Sheldon, a Californian doctor who conducted a great many studies of accidents, found that the Cadillac had

> a prominent knife-like projection just above the instrument panel. It was designed to prevent reflection of the instrument lights onto the windshield. To accomplish this minor task, they have produced as lethal a device as is seen on any American car. Chrysler has added a new gear shift lever that projects straight out from the dashboard. This defies all concepts of passenger safety.

Tragically, a brave attempt by Ford or, more precisely, by Robert McNamara, to promote safer cars was ruthlessly crushed. The future Secretary for Defense and President of the World Bank first became famous during the 1950s as the brightest of the group of whiz-kids assembled by Henry Ford II to rebuild the company founded and nearly wrecked by his grandfather. Until the mid-1950s McNamara had subscribed to the general industry view that drivers were to blame for accidents, and had absorbed the basic lesson of the post-war car market that only style sold.

Today he makes a contrast between Plymouth and Cadillac in the 1950s. 'Plymouth was headed by an engineer and the result was that the first post-war Plymouth was an engineer's dream. It was designed toward function and it was marketed as such as "Bigger on the inside, smaller on the outside, efficiency, economy, function." In contrast GM did exactly the opposite and their premier car, the Cadillac, came out with monstrous fins – masses of non-functional metal. At Ford we thought heads would roll in the General Motors building, that the manager of Cadillac would be fired. Instead the Plymouth was a dud, it didn't sell. The Cadillac set the style for the industry for two decades, non-functional glorification of one's income, an appeal to conspicuous consumption.

'In the early 1950s when I began to examine the problem of automobile safety I found that roughly 45,000 people per year were being killed in automobile accidents. To put that in perspective that's roughly the same number as were killed in total in the Vietnam war in the American military forces over a thirteen-year period and yet at the time, in the 1950s, it was thought very little could be done about the automobile accidents.' But his mind was changed by visits paid by Ford's chief safety engineer, Alex Haynes to see the ACIR programme. McNamara immediately saw the point they were making, that 'if the occupants of the car were packaged correctly the fatalities and the injuries could be greatly reduced. They drew an analogy between packaging eggs in a paper bag on the one hand versus packaging in an egg carton on the other and they said, what we all know, that the eggs in a bag will break much more easily than those in a carton and they said that if you package the occupants of a car in the equivalent of a carton, they won't be injured to the degree they are today. They began to experiment, to develop the proper packaging, and they needed money for this, they were operating on a shoestring. They were literally dropping human skulls packaged in different ways down the stairwells of Cornell's student dormitories, that was their lab. They needed money, so I decided to try to raise the money – a few hundred thousand dollars – in the auto industry. Ford agreed to contribute, I've forgotten what but let's say a hundred or two hundred thousand dollars, Chrysler put in a few tens of thousands, GM refused. They weren't interested one damned bit in safety, they didn't feel they had a societal responsibility to address the problem.'

The result was that the 1956 Fords included 'a package of safety features which included a collapsible steering wheel that absorbed the impact and prevented the chest from being torn apart by the steering column, and door-locks so that the doors would not spring open in a crash spilling the occupants out on the street. They included padded sun visors and padded instrument panels to prevent head injuries and, perhaps most importantly, they included seat-belts. It took about two years to design the car and during the design process our competitors learnt we were introducing the features and they incorporated them in their models as well, so all three manufacturers came out with 1956 models carrying safety features in roughly September 1955. In the case of Ford we marketed these as our Lifeguard design.'

This initiative by a mainstream motor manufacturer was revolutionary. Previously the only manufacturers who had tried to employ safety as a selling point had been marginal, like Kaiser-Frazer or the wretched Preston Tucker, who went broke in 1948 before his safety car went into production. The rest of the industry was sceptical, not only of the features themselves but that Ford was actually promoting them. McNamara, by then general manager of the Ford car division, had managed to persuade Henry Ford II to price the seat-belts, for example, at slightly below cost: 'I promoted the safety features, the Lifeguard features, very heavily', and Ford even circulated comparative photographs of their cars and Chevrolets in crashes. As a result the 'safety extras' sold even better than he had hoped.

Yet even within the company itself McNamara faced strong opposition. He recalls how on one visit to Ford's plant in Dallas, Texas, 'The manager met me at the airport. I got into the passenger seat in the front of the car and I saw him looking out of the corner of his eye at me when I buckled on my seat-belt and finally he could contain himself no longer. He said, "What the hell's the matter with you? Are you afraid of my driving?" Now that epitomized the attitude not just of this manager in that case but certainly of the industry and to some degree of the public.' Nevertheless McNamara was deluged with letters from people whose lives had been saved. In one case 'a couple driving in a Thunderbird car on a long stretch of road on the east side of the Sierras in California and they were driving about 70 miles an hour. They hit a dog, the Thunderbird flipped over into a ditch, the two people unbuckled their belts and walked away from it.'

GM's reaction was immediate and deadly. Unbeknown to McNamara, Harlow Curtice, then its president, 'instructed one of his officers to call Walker Williams, the vice-president in charge of sales of the whole Ford Motor Company, to instruct me to call off the promotion of safety. GM feared promoting safety would draw attention to the risk of accidents and reduce car sales, to me an absolutely absurd position but that was the position in the industry. It sounds absurd, it certainly sounded absurd to me, but they believed it so strongly they put tremendous pressure on Ford to force a reduction in our emphasis on safety. They thought it would take the romance, if you will, out of car buying – insane.'

Ralph Nader believes that GM's opposition was based on wider considerations, that GM 'told Ford that they could be inviting greater public scrutiny that would lead to federal safety regulation. Second, they were saying to Ford that by highlighting the safety features Ford and other companies may be inviting lawsuits by injured people who would say they were injured because the company didn't put a safety feature in a car that they had on the shelf. I think they were concerned that the customer would start looking at the car functionally and start asking questions about safety, which could lead to fuel efficiency, which could lead to the excessive repair costs of the cars. They wanted customers to ask questions about style and horsepower and comfort and various kinds of options that were expensive and profitable. They didn't want to get the customer in a safety frame of mind.'

McNamara still believes that he 'could prove that we sold about a hundred to two hundred thousand more 1956 model Fords because of our promotion of safety than we would have sold had we not. However, in competitive terms versus the Chevrolet, the car did not sell well. I think it was because the public preferred the Chevrolet styling, but the result was that the conventional wisdom in the industry – represented, for example, by a statement in the *Automotive News*, the trade paper of the industry, in the spring of 1956 – was that 'McNamara sold safety and Chevrolet sold cars'; and that conventional wisdom prevailed for years. It took about twenty years, from roughly 1955 to 1975, to obtain any reasonable degree of use of seat-belts.' Nevertheless McNamara still believes that 'We had done something important. We had started people thinking that, OK, an accident might be the driver's fault, but maybe you could protect him a little from his own mistakes.'

For his part, John Telnack, the Ford designer, puts the responsibility squarely on the buying public of the day: 'There's no question about it, in the mid-fifties when we first introduced safety, we couldn't sell it. The public didn't want it and the buyers really determine the market out there. They know what they want and we have to give it to them. I mean, it's just like fins. They demanded fins and we had to give them fins. They demanded a lot of chrome in those days, too. Now you might say, "Well, the designers started adding all that chrome to cars in the first place," and I'm not sure which came first, but the buyer is the final determinant in the success of any automobile or any product.'

Typically, GM fought an effective rearguard action in ensuring that seat-belts were not fitted in cars as standard equipment until 1964 – nine years after Chrysler and Ford had offered them – and then as an optional extra.

Even that was six years after the much smaller firm American Motors had tried to install them as standard equipment. But, as Roy Abernethy, later president of American Motors, remarked, 'We ran into so much apathy – and actual resistance – that we were forced to drop the feature.' The key to the industry's opposition to the belts was simplicity itself: it reminded people of the dangers inherent in the *second* collision – between the occupant and the car's interior. Nevertheless by the early 1960s a number of states, led by New York, had started to insist on their installation.

What sold, of course, as John Telnach said, was style and speed. The latter was provided by the high-compression V-8 engines, introduced by GM in the early 1950s, which led *Consumer Reports* to argue that it was dangerous to drop 'all this power into vehicles that do not handle, steer, stop or hold the road as high-powered cars should do'. In the early 1960s the horsepower race was exacerbated by Ford's return to motor-racing – and attracted criticism from Senator Abe Ribicoff, an early congressional critic of the industry. However, like so many other initiatives of the time, the protests fell into empty space.

Ironically, the greatest single triumph of what can only be called the 'packagers' came from McNamara's successor, Lee Iacocca, with the Mustang, the greatest low-cost status symbol in the history of the industry. As John Telnack, one of the design team, puts it, 'It had a sportiness about it but it was a sporty elegance. It wasn't just an all-out race sportiness but the kind of sportiness that people felt very comfortable with and one that they could identify with.' The name helped in associating the car with the freedom of the Wild West, but its appeal, above all to young American males, was overtly sexual – indeed, it is not too much of an exaggeration to call the Mustang, with its long low bonnet, 'the greatest penis substitute of them all'. (One woman actually wrote to Ford to say that 'The Mustang is as exciting as sex.') And the 'wild Mustang' proved no passing fad: it was one of Ford's most long-lasting successes. Its sales were seemingly unaffected by road tests that said it abounded 'with new and startling engineering features carried over from 1910', resulting in a car which was a 'heavy-nosed blunderbuss with a teenage rear suspension'. (Ford removed from the production model a number of safety improvements it had included, at no great cost, in the original version.)

The Mustang was not unique, merely the extreme example of a general policy of neglecting safety factors in favour of power, styling and sheer flash. In 1965 Buick was advertising its Skylark Gran Sport under the headline 'Son of Gun' with the amazing text: 'Ever prodded a throttle with 445 pound-feet of torque coiled tightly at the end of it? Do that with one of these and you can start billing yourself as the Human Cannonball.'

Even when some dangerous external feature, such as the prominent knife-like tail fins, which reached their apotheosis in the 1959 Cadillac, was eliminated, this happened because styles had changed, and certainly not because safety considerations had entered into the design equation. The stylists, and their bosses, were unaware of the conclusions of two eminent doctors that 'If one were to attempt to produce a pedestrian-injuring mechanism, one of the most theoretically efficient designs which might be developed would closely approach that of the front end of some present-day automobiles.'

The neglect was not only American. When a distinguished American optometrist investigated vehicles to see if the visibility they offered was impaired by the reflections from the windscreen and instrument panels, he discovered that none of the cars he tested, either American or European, 'could provide a suitable visual environment for daytime driving'. Matters were made worse by the wrap-around windscreen, introduced with much fanfare by GM in 1954, which induced what one expert described as 'terrific visual distortion'. Tinted windscreens were even worse because they reduced the driver's vision so sharply.

The problems were well enough known, but only to the experts. Ross McFarland, a professor at Harvard, had stated them succinctly: 'In general, any control difficult to reach or operate, any instrument dial of poor legibility, any seat inducing poor posture or discomfort, or any unnecessary obstruction to vision may contribute directly to an accident.' In this state of affairs, a major advance – like the belated introduction of disc brakes on some 1965 models – could be treated as simply another gimmick. The S word was totally *verboten*.

So, indeed, was the P word. Pollution. As early as 1950 a distinguished Californian biochemist, Dr Arlie Haagen-Smit, had established the link between car exhausts and the smog already building up in Los Angeles, the way that, particularly in sunny weather, the hydrocarbon compounds in the exhausts reacted with the nitrogen in the air to produce the photochemical smog now so familiar to city-dwellers the world over. California acted alone: by 1966 the state had legislated for exhaust controls on all vehicles sold there, standards met by some manufacturers through the use of a pump injecting air directly into the exhaust – a method first patented back in 1909.

Even then, and ignoring the growing evidence that the smog epidemic had spread to most other urban areas, the manufacturers told an increasingly irritable Senator Abe Ribicoff that conditions elsewhere did not warrant any national effort. At the time, of course, they could rely on a generally apathetic public. In Nader's words: 'The manufacturers have two basic criteria for judging a potential design change: 1/ will it reduce costs? 2/ will it increase sales? The automobile makers seem to have decided that cleaning up exhausts will do neither.' (Nader was exaggerating. In 1959 the manufacturers announced that they had 'discovered' – which they must have known for years – that emissions from automobile crankcases were a major source of hydrocarbons and that they would install ventilation systems in the 1961 models they were still selling in California. Purely coincidentally, of course, the Californians had passed a law requiring such a system by that date.)

During the 1950s only one congressman, Kenneth Roberts from Alabama, normally a believer in minimal government, made any real effort to control the industry. His first hearings, held in 1956, set a pattern of industry arrogance – and public indifference – that lasted for nearly a decade. But, not surprisingly, attempts to get elementary legislation on to the statute book were unsuccessful. One particular case concerned the way in which some brake fluids vapourized at a dangerously low temperature, causing the brakes to fail. But, inevitably, once the resulting accident was investigated, the temperature had fallen enough for the fluid to retain its normal texture: the evidence had simply liquified. Roberts was even frustrated when he suggested that the vehicles purchased by the General Services Administration (GSA) on behalf of the government complied with some basic safety criteria. The motor industry simply ensured that they were so watered down as to be virtually meaningless.

The limit of achievable improvements was well shown in 1963 when Chrysler introduced a newly refined engine that reduced emissions by two-thirds, thanks to a series of well thought-out modifications. This was welcomed by the Los Angeles Air Pollution Control District (APCD), which ensured that only such vehicles would be bought by the local government. But the other manufacturers put such pressure on Chrysler that it dared not advertise this first genuinely successful attempt to reduce the increasing pollution from motor vehicles.

But more important was the conversion of politicians in a number of states, starting with New York, to the idea of installing anchorages for seat-belts. (When one manufacturer claimed that a lot of people objected to them John Moore, a former director of the Cornell project, replied drily that: 'No safety device can be used by the public unless it is first made available to the public.') The industry's opposition to belts was hardened by the growing popularity of hardtops and convertibles, which had come to account for up to half the sales of all new cars. Their construction made it difficult, if not impossible, to fit the anchorages required for anything more than the simplest lap-belt – and the problem was exacerbated because virtually all cars manufactured at the time had bench seats in the front with room for three occupants.

During the first half of the 1960s the atmosphere changed and an increasing number of voices could be heard attacking the industry with greater or lesser degrees of success. Not that GM showed any sign of weakening: in 1961 John Gordon, then the company's president, told the

National Safety Congress that those demanding federal regulation of car design were talking of an entirely 'foolproof and crash-proof car', an obviously absurd Aunt Sally which Gordon had no difficulty in demolishing. His company could even afford to ignore a book published a year later, *The Highway Jungle* by Edward A. Tenny, even though the author pointed out quite rightly that sales pressure from the industry was landing the country's roads with far too many cars, that 'the problem is much too big for private control and the conspicuous failures in Engineering, Education, Enforcement, buttress this argument'.

Still, there was some progress. In 1963 a New York state senator, Edward Speno, had reduced an industry audience to a state of stunned silence by proposing a minimum safety standard for tyres. Two years later, when Senator Gaylord Nelson introduced a bill covering the same ground in the Senate, his initiative was greeted with applause. A telegram from one California tyre dealer read: 'Many motorists are riding on a time bomb.' In the hearings that followed it became clear that the problem lay not with the tyre manufacturers but with the all-powerful car manufacturers. The ground had been well prepared, and both Congress and the general public were now eager to seize on any serious evidence that the industry was playing games with people's lives.

Until then there had been little or no pressure on legislators to act on safety. At the presidential level Eisenhower was succeeded by John F. Kennedy who, in a typically grandiose declaration, proclaimed that traffic accidents were 'one of the greatest, perhaps the greatest of the nation's public health problems', but, equally typically, he did nothing during his short presidency to address the problem.

But by 1965, when the GSA published its safety criteria, the industry's solid front was beginning to crack. Early in 1963, Sherwood Egbert, President of Studebaker, one of the smallest manufacturers, had already said the unsayable. After announcing that his company would install seat-belts (and not just anchorages for them) in every car made after February that year he said that it was his company's 'strong feeling that safety measures in motor-cars should not come by petition from motorists but that automobile manufacturers should lead in safety equipment'. This, of course, was the purest heresy: the industry had always made a point of *following* on safety matters because of the supposedly horrendous cost of complying with even the simplest requirements – a ridiculous defence at a time when models were changed every year at a cost estimated at $700 per car, even though the changes were almost invariably cosmetic. By contrast the industry was spending a mere $2 million per year on safety – or 23 cents for every car it produced.

These figures were published in 1965, a couple of weeks after the GSA had set its safety standards, in the course of the first-ever hearings on car safety in the Senate.* GM had tried to placate the committee by announcing a gift of $1 million for safety research, but neither of the corporation's top men, the chairman, Frederic Donner, and the president, James Roche, was prepared for the hostility of the questioning they underwent, above all from Bobby Kennedy, who had just been elected as senator for that most safety-conscious of states New York, and who compared GM's $1 million with their annual profits of $1.7 billion. The industry promptly started to make promises – albeit vague ones – to increase its attention to safety standards. Similar pressure was building up through Senator Gaylord Nelson and through the Federal Trade Commission (FTC), both concerned with a long-standing scandal: the habit of car manufacturers of fitting undersized tyres that required excessive pressures to bear the car's weight and were thus liable to blow out within a few hundred miles.

Earlier in 1965 a television documentary called *Death on the Highway* highlighted the specific dangers inherent in some popular vehicles, although only for the benefit of the relatively restricted numbers of viewers who watched National Educational Television channels.

The time was right for a breakthrough and this came from an unlikely source, a book by a young lawyer, Ralph Nader – 'He happened to be spurring a horse at just the right instant,' is the way John Stapp puts it. Nader, a Harvard law graduate already interested in road safety, had joined Daniel Patrick Moynihan's research staff in the spring of 1965. Today Nader tends to turn his back on his predecessors' work. He prefers to concentrate on personal experience, how, during his college years he 'used to hitchhike a great deal, both back and forth from home and during vacations all over the United States. I'd be picked up by trucks and truck drivers who would often be first at the scene of some pretty horrible crashes and we'd rush to the scene, sometimes before the police got there. One time I saw a particularly gruesome crash in New England where a young child had been decapitated and I realized that the sharp edge of the glove compartment door was the instrument. I began to look at the evidence in engineering studies from the Harvard School of Public Health on human factors and crashworthiness.'

As a result Nader 'decided to write a paper in my personal injury law class called "Medical Legal Seminar on Automobile Design and Legal Liability". In the process of researching it I uncovered all kinds of proven safety features that were on the shelf in the auto companies factories but not put into cars. So I saw a great opportunity to push for safer cars in order to save lives. When reporters asked my mother, "Why is Ralph doing this?" she was totally nonplussed. She said, "Do you mean why is Ralph working to try to

*Through a sub-committee on, of all things, executive reorganization.

save lives?" I mean, why wouldn't anybody try to work to save lives? When Senator Robert Kennedy asked me this very question, "Why are you doing this?" I said, "If I was engaged in advancing the prevention of cruelty to animals nobody would ask me what my motivation was but I'm engaged in advancing the prevention of cruelty to humans." '

Many of the improvements Nader wrote about were not new. 'The collapsible steering column had been patented before World War One, seat-belts were available in aviation before and during World War One to keep the pilots in the plane from falling out. The padded dash panel was never even patented – it's just common sense. You need stronger seat anchorages to keep the seat from ripping up and hurling you through the windshield in a collision. *That's* just common sense. They used to build chariots like that centuries ago. Stronger door latches to keep you from being thrown out onto hard pavement – again common sense, with the engineering available for over a century.'

His book, *Unsafe at Any Speed,* had an enormous impact – it remained in print for several decades – summed up in a review written by the late Lewis Mumford, town-planner and visionary: 'The present [American] motor car has been the result of a secret collaboration between the beautician and the mortician; and, according to sales and accident statistics, both have reason to be satisfied.'

To the Great American Public the biggest shock came from Nader's revelations of the dangers in one particular model: the Chevrolet Corvair, a compact car originally introduced in September 1959. In the past, as Nader points out: 'There had been some criticism of automobile safety but it was very general, there weren't any proper names, there was no company allocation of responsibility by model. The Corvair was a uniquely hazardous car. It had an instability factor built into it that was preventable and knowable by GM, which ignored the way to do it properly. It had a carbon monoxide leakage problem, and it had a propensity for the steering column to jam back into the driver's chest in a very low right front collision. There was a lot more documentation on the Corvair because it was the subject of litigation in US courts in several states.'

Ironically, the Corvair was GM's imaginative response to complaints that its cars were environmentally unfriendly gas guzzlers, and, more importantly, to the increasing success of the VW Beetle. It was the brain-child of Ed Cole, an unusually innovative engineer who had started work at GM in the 1930s when it was the most exciting engineering company in the world. In engineering terms a vehicle with a rear-mounted, air-cooled aluminium engine was a far more imaginative initiative than anything that GM had come up with since the 1930s and provided much more room within the dimensions of what Americans would call a compact car – although, by European standards, such cars would be classed as 'large family saloons'. In many ways, it was a brilliant solution to the problem of creating a car of modest overall dimensions which offered minimal fuel consumption (by American standards, anyway) and provided accommodation for six occupants.

But the car had to be economical to produce, and certain features were eliminated that might not have been important in a vehicle with an orthodox front-engine rear-drive layout, but which were, literally, fatal when applied to the Corvair. The unorthodox layout gave rise to a number of problems: the car was heated by air that had been used to cool the engine, which left open the possibility that dangerous fumes from the engine would enter the passenger compartment.* But it was the design of the rear suspension that caused by far the most trouble. Early on GM knew that it was faulty. Tests had proved right the warnings of Maurice Olley, the company's greatest expert on automotive handling behaviour: he had published a criticism of rear-engined cars with swing-axle rear suspension and was also worried that mounting the fuel tank in the front of the car greatly increased the risks involved in any collision.

The Corvair, like any car with its engine – and thus the bulk of its weight – on the back axles, is inherently liable to 'oversteer', that is, the car will go further in the direction in which it is pointing than would seem normal from the degree to which the driver has turned the wheel. This condition is far less stable than its opposite, 'under-steer', in which the car turns less sharply than the movement of the steering wheel. In *Unsafe at Any Speed*, Nader quotes Ocee Ritch, a well-known Californian tester, who described the problems graphically. When cornering, the Corvair's

> rear starts to swing outward. The rear tires dig in but the shift in weight places them in rather odd angles relative to the pavement. These angles are great enough to increase steering force and, suddenly, the car is negotiating a tighter curve than intended. Another problem with the Corvair is extreme sensitivity to cross winds. If a sudden gust hits the car, it causes the rear to sway rather severely.

Originally GM had planned to introduce a stabilizer bar but omitted the refinement to save $4 a vehicle.

The problem was simple, and similar to that encountered in other cars with rear engines, like the VW Beetle and the British Triumph Herald. The fact that the links between the drive-shafts and the wheels were simply too loose sharply reduced the driver's control on corners or on irregular or

---

*In water-cooled cars, of course, this is impossible since the air is heated separately.

slippery surfaces. The Beetle, in particular, was notoriously liable to accidents under these conditions, which did not stop VW from producing a brilliant, and brilliantly dishonest, TV commercial showing a Beetle driving over a snowy field to reach a snow-plough. The only commentary was 'Did you ever think how the driver of the snow-plough *gets* to the snow-plough?' Indeed, Nader's failure to attack the Beetle – and his subsequent neglect of the dangers inherent in other imported vehicles – shows that his attack was as much on unchallenged corporate power as on a particular vehicle. 'Coming from General Motors,' he wrote, 'such behaviour – and the fact that it is tolerated – is a syndrome [did he mean symptom?] of a much deeper malaise that radiates beyond corporate orders and into society.'

Nevertheless, the handling problems caused by the swing-axle design were far worse on the Corvair than on comparable European cars because it was so much bigger, heavier, and therefore so much more difficult to control. Moreover, as Nader pointed out, the Corvair alone suffered from 'the sudden onset of the critical point at which the vehicle goes out of control and frequently flips over'. As Robert Janeway, a Chrysler engineer, pointed out at the time, 'Critical speeds can occur in the normal driving-speed range on sharp curves even at moderate degrees of oversteer.' As Nader wrote: 'Other makes of vehicle can be made to oversteer through drastic tire inflation differentials, or very heavy loading, but as the forces produced mount towards the critical point, they give a warning to the driver in the "feedback" he receives through the steering wheel, if indeed he is not forewarned by the under-inflated tyres before or as he gets underway.' But not the Corvair. Nader added,

> In ways wholly unique, the Corvair can become an aggressive, single-minded machine. One factor has been noticed in many single-car Corvair upsets. This is where the rear wheel tucks under so far that the rim touches the roadway. When this occurs no driver can control the vehicle, which will be lifted up and very likely turns over. Rim scrapings or gouge marks on the road have become the macabre trademark of Corvairs going unexpectedly out of control.

GM's engineers had tried to reduce the impact of the design problems by requiring tyre pressures of 15 lbs per square inch (psi) on the front tyres and 26 psi on the rear wheel, a far greater difference than that encountered on any major production car before or since – and some experts were prepared to argue that even that was not sufficient. Yet although the difference was critical to the car's performance, GM was reluctant to spell out how essential it was since such a warning would have drawn attention to the car's inherent instability. (One dealer explained loftily that 'Cars are like women, they're all different.') GM only made matters worse when it placed the spare tyre for the 1961 Corvair Monza in the rear compartment, thus ensuring that when it was used its pressure would have risen and fallen with the temperature of the engine compartment and would have been unpredictable. Naturally GM did not suggest carrying anything so practical as a tyre-pressure gauge.

However, the 1964 model was improved, the addition of a transverse rear spring in particular greatly reducing the tuck-under hazard. (This could have been done much earlier, since the improvement dated back to experimental work undertaken by GM as far back as the 1930s.) In the autumn of 1964 the introduction of the 1965 models enabled commentators at the time to expatiate on the faults of earlier versions – which they had failed to mention because of GM's enormous clout. The magazine *Car & Driver* finally let the cat out of the bag:

> Despite a widespread misconception that the old Corvair was 'almost' a sports car, it was one of the nastiest-handling vehicles ever built. The tail gave little warning that it was about to let go, and when it did, it let go with a vengeance few drivers could cope with. The rear wheels would lose traction, tuck under, and with the tail end jacked up in the air, the car would swing around like a three-pound hammer on a thirty-foot string. This is not to say the car was unstable within the limits of everyday, fair-weather driving – just that these limits were none too clearly posted and, once transgressed, you were in pretty hairy territory indeed. The new Corvair handles altogether differently from its predecessors.

For the 1965 model* GM took out the swing axles. With proper linkages and fully flexible 'universal joints' the car enjoyed proper independent suspension so that the wheels did not automatically 'tuck in' under the car when it hit a bump or other impediment. The change did not come a moment too soon for GM. By the time the new suspension had been introduced, GM, unable to afford the publicity of a public hearing, was being forced to settle, out of court, cases brought because of deaths and injuries in crashes due to the instability of Corvairs built in the previous five years.

Nader's book proved to be an eminently successful attempt to convert the Great American Public to the idea that the automobile industry was not sacrosanct, that it could and should be regulated like any other member of the business community. For GM's policy over the Corvair, not just the

---

*Ironically, all GM's 1965 models were found to be shoddily made. All the cars tested by the independent research group Consumers Union displayed major manufacturing faults after being driven a mere 5000 miles.

car's design but also the corporation's stony refusal to admit any form of responsibility for its defects, was not unusual: Nader quotes the Buicks produced in the early 1950s with brake defects, and, as one trial judge remarked in one of the many cases involving accidents due to the defect: 'Defendant's Buick division warned its dealers. It did not warn those into whose hands they had placed this dangerous instrument and whose lives (along with the lives of others) depended upon defective brakes which might fail without notice.'

General Motors' first reaction to *Unsafe at Any Speed* had been to invite Nader to work for them. When he refused, they set the detectives on him, first in an attempt to prove that he was involved in one or more of the many legal cases outstanding against GM and then, when that tactic failed, to watch his every movement in the hope of otherwise discrediting him. The private eyes were eventually caught in the US Senate Office building and apprehended under a law that prevents a witness before a congressional committee from being harassed.

That incident, and GM's involvement, proved the catalyst for action. President Lyndon Johnson professed himself shaken by the evidence and by the public outcry at GM's behaviour: 'Highway deaths are second only to the Vietnam war as the gravest problem before the nation,' he said and, unlike his predecessor, acted decisively. GM was denounced on the floor of the Senate – a previously unthinkable phenomenon – and within six months, an unheard-of burst of speed by the standards of the US Congress, the industry had been brought within the federal regulatory network through the National Traffic and Motor Vehicle Safety Act, which in 1967 set up the National Traffic Safety Bureau, now the National Highway Traffic Safety Administration (NHTSA) after an executive reorganization in late 1970, which was responsible for implementing the safety standards set at the same time. Another piece of legislation passed at the same time, the Highway Safety Act, helped improve safety efforts at state level.

3

Highway to Safety
II: Enforcement – But of What?

The passage of the two acts was an historic turning-point. By no coincidence that same year, 1966, saw a decline in both the US and Europe of casualties, at least in relation to the number of vehicles on the road. As Elizabeth Drew put it, in *Atlantic Monthly*, the legislation represented 'a radical departure from the government's traditional, hands-off approach to the automobile industry, an industry which politician and businessman alike had long considered sacrosanct'. But it was not due entirely to the efforts of Nader and his supporters. As John D. Graham says in his book *Autosafety*: 'The passage of the 1966 Safety Act was as much a failure of corporate strategy as a success of the consumer movement.'

Nader's assault was merely the last battle in a war whose final stages made it clear that federal control had come to be seen as inevitable. As he wrote: 'For the first time the industry has lost its monopolistic control over an automotive safety system in its developmental stage, and with it has sacrificed its total control over whether or when the improvement will be introduced.'

Psychologically it represented just as considerable a swing away from the doctrine that, as John Graham observed, 'Crash-related injuries were primarily a behavioural problem. The driver in particular was seen as the causative agent in most crashes.' Previously, as Graham pointed out, the revelation of faults had been left to individuals who brought cases before the courts, 'a severe commentary,' as he said, 'on how superficially our society evaluates the vehicle's role in accident and injuries. It contrasts sharply with rail, air and marine design hazards which are meticulously investigated and publicly documented by government authorities.'

In an astonishingly short time Nader had succeeded in his object: to bring the all-powerful automobile industry within an effective federal regulatory net. His three-point programme had involved 'the stage of public awareness and demand for action, the stage of legislation, and the stage of continuing administration'. Two had been achieved within a few months. The third took longer. For the establishment of the NHSB was only the opening battle of nearly a quarter of a century of Car Wars between the industry and the authorities. For much of the following quarter of a century – with the notable exception of the period of Jimmy Carter's presidency – the new agency lacked the support it required from its superiors to convince public opinion.

The battle was complex, and cannot be portrayed simply as that of the people against the forces of blindly greedy capitalism (as we shall see, the insurance industry, the most emblematic of finance capitalism, played an important role in helping make cars safer, albeit for its own interests).

Despite his apparent success, Nader continued on his confrontational way. He assembled a group of young acolytes – Nader's Raiders – who worked on the whole field of consumer protection, including motors. He went on to publish the so-called *Lemon Book*, which advised people on what to do with unsatisfactory cars, and led to so-called 'Lemon Laws' being passed in a number of states giving better rights to purchasers of new automobiles. (In the past few years the Center for Auto Safety, founded under the inspiration of Clarence Ditlow, his most important associate, has published a magazine *Lemon Times*, devoted to the continuing pursuit of auto safety.)

John Stapp, however, became an apostle of the voluntary, co-operative approach. Looking back he says that 'Nader took the negative approach with the result that the Department of Transportation came into existence and at the same time there was a radical revolution in the industry toward safety. It was at that time that General Motors appointed a very wise, very safety-minded vice-president to be in charge of their safety and they went into research furiously on crashing their automobiles and all that sort of thing.' He could point to the many safety improvements, notably energy-absorbing steering columns, better windshields and less obtrusive instrument panels which added up to a considerable saving of lives in the years after the acts were passed.

Stapp took his safety ideas to the world in the form of what one can only describe as a crusade. In contrast to Nader, he says, 'I took the positive approach because I have one maxim by which I have lived. It's found in the twelfth chapter of the Epistle to the Romans, by my namesake Paul, twenty-first verse, and it says, "Resist not evil but overcome evil with good," and I was advocating what to do and the industry made me a member of that Society of Automotive Engineers, later a fellow in it and last April set up a foundation in my name for training engineers for safety. They found that safety was extremely profitable.' According to him, GM found that 'an air-bag inserted in a steering wheel at an immediate cost of about $35 could add $600 to the price of the car. That's better than beauty. The whole idea of safety in the engineering world was promoted by the annual Stapp car-crash conference of the Society of Automotive Engineers, of which I'm permanent chairman. From it came a medical association called the Association for Advancement of Automotive Medicine and in Europe an international research conference on bio-mechanics, the name they gave to this science of banging people and finding how much they'd take before they came to pieces. All of this has grown out of the seventy-three experiments we did with humans and eighty-five with animals on the track, and the thousands of experiments we did with other devices including a portable sling-shot seat that could be carried by airplane, taken to fairs. There people were given about a 7-G ride and stopped with mechanical friction brakes to feel their impingement against the restraints that we provided and that encouraged people to use the safety-belts.'

Nevertheless, as John Telnack points out, it took some time for the industry to absorb these new safety features into the design of its cars, if only because of the time-lag involved, which in the 1960s could be as much as five years. 'The government mandated a number of safety features. These got a little difficult to design around initially because we were trying to just add these safety features into existing cars. Once we had a clean piece of paper, an all-new car, an all-new platform to work with from the beginning, we were able to design the safety features into the cars and integrate them into the cars to give a total look, a total shape and it worked much better. I think probably the best example of that would be the safety bumpers that we introduced on our cars, say, in the mid to late seventies. They really looked like hang-on bumpers, like an afterthought, and they were, in fact, because we had to move very quickly to meet these safety regulations with bumpers but once we had new sheet metal and new cars and new platforms to work with, we were able to design the safety features into the cars in a much more integrated way and get a much better-looking car.'

The agency itself was perpetually short of funds and admitted that it depended to an unhealthy degree on the goodwill of the industry it was supposed to be regulating, if only because the manufacturers had more money, more expertise, and more access to those who wielded power in Washington than any single federal agency. And unfortunately (unlike Nader and his Raiders), it was unable to influence the Washington press corps or Congress, which – with the notable exception of representatives from the motor manufacturing states, most obviously Michigan – was basically friendly to the agency in its battle against its opponents. Also, the job of Secretary for Transportation was relatively lowly, and usually resembled a rotating door: in the twenty-one years after the Act was passed, there were no fewer than nine occupiers of the post, and seven heads of the NHSB/NHTSA. Such transient figures could not hope to compete with the well-entrenched bosses of the automobile companies. Nevertheless, the

NHTSA had clearly come to stay, and the motor companies had to resign themselves to dealing with it.

The shape of things to come could be seen as soon as the NHSB's first director, Dr William Haddon, set safety standards. Inevitably these were attacked from both sides, by the industry as too severe and by Nader and his supporters as inadequate. (Haddon's influence was felt well after he left the bureau through his work as a consultant and through his influential belief in passive rather than active restraint systems.)

Yet despite its inadequacies the existence of the bureau was an enormous help. From its inception the NHSB was useful in exposing myths previously spread by manufacturers about survivability: it gave the proof, for instance, that primates could survive crashes at over 80 m.p.h. whereas GM had confidently asserted that no one could survive a crash at over 35 m.p.h. It enjoyed a handful of early triumphs, notably in 1971 by forcing GM to recall over 6.5 million Chevrolets because of the dangers posed to the vehicle's stability by a defective front engine mounting, although even here it had required the support of a massive public outcry, encouraged by the arrogantly misleading claim by GM's president Ed Cole that 'It's no different from having a flat tire or a blow-out where you don't expect it.' In fact, the design fault had caused hundreds of deaths before the belated recall campaign.

The agency's existence also emboldened less official guardians of the public interest. In 1969 the Consumers' Union and the Insurance Institute for Highway Safety (IIHS), which played an increasingly important role promoting safety over the next fifteen years, began to test the relationship of the design of bumpers to property damage. They found, to no one's surprise that, in the words of Dr Haddon, then IIHS president, the manufacturers deliberately designed the 'largely cosmetic egg-shell front and rear ends of new automobiles to build up "huge sales in crash replacement parts"' which were, at the time, available only at excessive prices from the manufacturers themselves.

The manufacturers managed to tone down or delay the introduction of many obvious safety devices – similar tactics to those employed by many other US industries in conflict with the federal regulatory authorities over the years. A typical outburst came from Henry Ford II in December 1970 when he claimed that his company was doing everything possible to meet the tough new standards for emissions due to come into force five years later. But, he added, 'It doesn't look, at this time, as though we'll be able to meet these rules, but if we can't, I'm sure the government will modify them, since we could be forced out of business as they now stand.'

The longest-running battles were not over the faults in individual models but over the provision of safety equipment. This posed a fundamental division between a 'manual' or 'active' system, epitomized by the seat-belt, and the 'passive' or 'automatic' systems, of which the air-bag was the most obvious example. Both, of course, proceeded from the same principle: that the occupants of a vehicle (most obviously those in the front seats) must not be in danger of being thrown out in a crash and must be protected from collision, if not contact, with potential sources of injury inside the vehicle, like the steering wheel and the dashboard.

The two types of protection warranted two different approaches. Outside the United States, car occupants could be expected to be, if not easy to discipline, at least capable of being disciplined by the police acting in the name of the state. Americans resent interference by the state even when the dangers of lack of control are blindingly obvious – as evidenced by the continuing power of the 'gun lobby' in the form of the National Rifle Association, which so successfully advocates total freedom when it comes to the purchase of weapons far more lethal than cars. Also, most Americans consider driving a car as natural as breathing. It is no coincidence that in California a driving licence acts as the only form of identity document – I've known non-drivers acquire one simply to have proof of their identity. So driving is simply an integral part of everyday life and should, therefore, involve as little effort as possible. Hence the ubiquity of automatic transmissions and the continuing opposition within the American public to seat-belts and the positive effort they involved.

American reluctance to accept compulsion of any sort, even for their own good, meant that while the rest of the world contented itself with fitting seat-belts and ensuring that they were worn, Americans had to find some more automatic device. In practice, that meant fitting air-bags, first to save the driver from the impact with the steering wheel, and then to help passengers.

Most of the arguments during the quarter-century that followed the passage of the Acts, are symbolized by the story of air-bags. In Ben Kelly's words, 'What has happened with air-bags is really very typical of and almost an allegory of what's gone wrong with automotive safety generally, why so little progress has been made and why there have been so many problems. The story of air-bags – and I could almost replace the word air-bag with seat-belts or some other safety aspect – is one of initial great promise as the technology developed. Then a backlash developed within the industry against the idea of a government requirement, which then becomes a backlash against the technology itself and a resistance to that technology, and a shifting of resources and interest and energy away from development and research and testing and positive things, to the negative things of opposing and legal opposition and spending money on lobbying and public relations against government. As a result we have air-bags on the highways fifteen years later than they should have been, full of problems that are hurting people, that should have been fixed and never should have been put in the cars in the first place. That's the story of air-bags and it's the story of most safety improvements.'

The principle, and the mechanism, of the air-bag seems to be simplicity itself. As John Graham describes it in *Autosafety*: 'Crash sensors in the structure of the car were set to trigger deployment mechanisms within the passenger compartment whenever deceleration forces in the forward direction exceeded five Gs [five times the force of gravity]. The deployment mechanisms would inflate large nylon cushions (stored within the steering wheel and instrument panel) into the car interior within four-hundredths of a second before the car occupants began to move forward. During the "second collision" occupants would strike the inflated nylon cushions instead of the steering wheel, dashboard or windshield. Holes in the end of the bag would cause the cushions to deflate rapidly after crash forces were absorbed,' so as not to encumber the occupants.

According to Ben Kelly: 'The first patents for what we can call an authentic air-bag date back probably as early as the 1940s.' As with seat-belts the first tests were done during the 1950s in aircraft. As far as cars were concerned the inventor Assen Jordonoff, and Dr Carl Clark, a biophysicist, first demonstrated air-bags in 1964 and 1965.

At first the idea was ridiculed, but within three years it was taken up by a number of important component manufacturers, notably Eaton, Yale & Towne, which worked with Ford, and Allied Chemical, working with General Motors. At that point, says Kelly, 'It was the belief of everybody who was seriously concerned with safety that within five to ten years of that point, say 1967 or '68, air-bags could be a reality in all new cars. Eaton and Allied went to work. In fact Eaton issued a documentary film – I believe in 1968 – in which it stated, after showing crash tests and other developmental work, that it was ready to provide manufacturers with a full front-seat air-bag system that would work marvellously. Eaton is a very serious company, so at that point the air-bag was on what I would call the reality track.'

Significantly, the mechanism, which Eaton, Yale & Towne called the 'Auto-Ceptor' was designed only to supplement lap-belts, which were needed to position the occupants so that the air-bags would hit them in the right place, although the mechanism would remove the need for the shoulder harnesses that the American motorist found particularly irritating. The mechanism was still primitive: it was expensive and the 5G trigger point was so low that the bag would inflate in accidents so minor that no injury was likely.

Ideally, both seat-belts and air-bags were necessary safety features partly because of the potential for injury that remained by using air-bags only – although they, like seat-belts, have saved far more lives than they have damaged or ended. As Jeff Crandall, of the Automobile Safety Laboratory in Virginia, points out, two-thirds of collisions are frontal collisions. In them, he says, 'If you've got an air-bag you still need a seat-belt. If you have the belt restraint, it holds back the shoulder and chest and allows rotation of the neck so that the head is positioned right in the centre of an air-bag. I'm a taller occupant: if I was in a crash unbelted and I had an air-bag, I have the potential to go over the air-bag and strike either the windshield or the header in the vehicle – so if I were in a crash without a belt there's a great likelihood that I would still get a head injury due to contact, that the air-bag could not protect me.'

Ben Kelly points out that 'The air-bag was developed initially in an environment where people weren't wearing safety-belts in this country.' Nevertheless, as he insists, 'Air-bags and seat-belts do very different things. They overlap somewhat, they provide protection in some of the same crash conditions, but in fact they provide very different kinds of protection under very different crash conditions and they complement each other. If you don't wear your seat-belt you're much better off with an air-bag overall, statistically and factually. However, the air-bag is more likely also to hurt you because of the energy of the deployment if you're not wearing your seat-belt. If you don't have an air-bag and you have a seat-belt and wear it, you're going to be well off in lower-velocity change crashes but you're not going to be well off in the higher-velocity change crashes where air-bags make a big difference, for belted or unbelted occupants. If you have both a properly designed seat-belt and a properly designed air-bag, then you are well protected in many of the common crash modes, including the higher-speed crash modes.'

But the sheer explosive force of the air-bag created problems that have not yet been completely overcome. As Kelly points out: 'The nature of the air-bag is that it has a tremendous amount of energy which is instantly, explosively released in a crash when the air-bag sensor tells it to fire. Now that energy can be hurtful if it is not properly applied. To use it properly the air-bag should be firing at different levels of intensity for different kinds, different speeds of crashes. It should be sensing the shape and size and nature of the person in the seat in front of the air-bag so that in the crash the air-bag will relate well to that person. It should be sensing whether the belt is being worn or not worn so that the air-bag won't come out and meet an unbelted occupant too soon and hurt that person in the face or the neck or whatever. All of these things are necessary to an adequately designed air-bag, and if they're not present, that tremendous explosive power in some cases, happily not many but all too many nonetheless, can hurt or kill people.'

But even today, as he says, 'The occupant is getting literally whacked by the air-bag as the air-bag is unfolding and deploying in this very rapid, explosive process, rather than the occupant moving into the fully inflated or almost inflated air-bag which is what's supposed to happen. Other problems are that the position of the occupant is such that the occupant is taking the blow of the air-bag other than distributed over the front of the face or the body, in a way that can hurt, for instance, the upper cervical spine, the head, what have you.'

For instance, 'A very small woman who is unable to reach the pedals of the car without having the seat all the way forward and perhaps even being pushed a little forward in her seat with a cushion behind her or under her. She's wearing her seat-belt but she's still very close to the steering wheel and now involved in a lower-speed impact. Nevertheless the bag goes off because it is pre-set at a level which anticipates crashes not only at 15 or 20 m.p.h. but at 30 m.p.h. and above, and so it's a fairly high level. So the woman whose head is "too close" to the air-bag is hurt by its impact – it literally smashes her in the head. Now the tests that the manufacturers have to run under government standards may not anticipate exactly the position she was in but we know in the real world that people will be in those positions and the air-bag design must accommodate them. How could it accommodate her? Perhaps by sensing the velocity change of the crash and firing the bag at a lower deployment level so that when it impacted her, it would not do it harmfully. Perhaps by sensing that she is in the seat and she's small and the bag should not be coming out so quickly or so fast or so hard. There are many ways to do it but without a commitment by the manufacturer to do it, it won't get done.'

Kelly is demanding what may be an unrealizable degree of sophistication, but Byron Bloch is surely right when he points to the relative lack of sophistication even in today's designs. 'They all inflate at a single high inflation pressure, and they come out of the instrument panel directly at the heads and chests of small children. Instead, the air-bag should inflate with a low pressure in the lower-speed crashes and then a higher pressure in the more severe crashes, and the air-bag should also be top-mounted on the upper part of the instrument panel so that when it initially comes out it is not so forcefully aimed right at the head of a small child. Air-bags can also prove dangerous, or even fatal, if the shape is wrong, if the inflation rate is too high, or if the levels are not different for each occupant, if the sensors are of the wrong kind or in the wrong place, if the vents used for deflating the bag are wrongly placed, or if the occupant is not aware how to sit in relation to the bag. In real life the fitting of bags for passenger seats has resulted in a number of well-publicized cases in which small children have had their necks snapped by bags. Even today Volvo, still probably the most safety-conscious of all manufacturers, warns owners never to place a child in a child seat or on a booster cushion in the front seat of a car equipped with a passenger-side air-bag.

One recent case, that of young Kyle Lehman, who was killed by the air-bag when in the front seat of her mother's car, caused enormous concern –

it was even featured on the network evening-news bulletins, the supreme accolade in the United States of newsworthiness. To make matters worse Mrs Lehman had bought a '95 Chevvy Alumina. 'Before we bought it we checked around for a safe car as we wanted to get a nice safe family car and we were told that Alumina was very safe, and we bought it because we figured, you know, the air-bag would save our lives and that it added extra protection even for Kyle up front.'

By 1970 a 'passive restraint' standard had been issued, which was meant to come into force the following October. This set off another argument, not, for once, between the government and the industry, but within the industry itself. Eaton Yale & Towne's perception of the air-bag was at odds with that of Ed Cole, the man behind the Corvair. In November 1967 Cole had been appointed President of GM, the second most powerful position in the group. Despite his setback over the Corvair he remained an enthusiastic supporter of new ideas – he was, for instance, a leading exponent of the Wankel rotary engine and, had it not been for the oil crisis of October 1973, might well have introduced it into some of GM's vehicles. He believed that air-bags could replace all other restraint mechanisms, and resented the emphasis being placed on seat-belts. But he had accepted the need for some form of federal regulation, reckoning that GM's superior technical resources would help it retain its lead over its rivals, whatever regulations were imposed.

Even the normally hypercritical Ben Kelly was impressed by Cole's programme: 'He pushed air-bag research, testing and development at General Motors and finally forced the company to begin selling air-bags in new cars. There was great resistance within the company to this idea and they held him to putting these in a very few cars and to virtually doing this with no marketing or advertising, but GM did put a good air-bag in those cars and those air-bags worked very well in crashes. Now at that point General Motors and others were able to talk about multi-stage air-bags, to talk about various configurations of low and high impact that would perhaps be sensitive to different sizes of occupants, to different crash speeds – in other words, air-bags that really did respond to the needs of that occupant at that time.'

The cause of safety was greatly boosted when President Richard Nixon appointed John Volpe as his first Secretary for Transportation. Although he was a right-wing Republican, Volpe was also a devout Catholic, a decent man who saw the NHSB as a home for 'people-oriented' programmes and recruited Douglas Toms, a safety expert from the state of Washington to head it. He came up with a clear policy, which John Graham defined as a plan that would: 'start with ambitious standards and strict deadlines, stimulate crash programmes of engineering work in Detroit, and then relax the timetable as appropriate when deadlines drew near. They refused to accept arguments that passive protection was infeasible or ill-advised.' But the strategy failed: it generated too much corporate resistance and Volpe and Toms did not have enough clout at the President's court to resist the opposition. Among the many other goodies revealed by the Watergate tapes was that Henry Ford and Lee Iacocca had urged Nixon to oppose Volpe's proposed law on air-bags. Their introduction was duly delayed for five years. Ford's attitude was no secret: he had been quoted on a number of occasions as saying that 'Air-bags are a lot of baloney.'

In the summer of 1972 the air-bag received a bad setback when one failed in the course of a public test. The cause was almost certainly accidental, but the atmosphere at the time was so poisonous that sabotage was suspected. To Ben Kelly the problem lay not with the air-bags but with the industry's opposition.

Byron Bloch points out that the 1973 Chevrolets had air-bags for both front-seat occupants. 'That's a quarter century ago and if all the car companies had continued with air-bags, like in this '73 car, all of the wrecked cars you see around you where the people were killed or horribly injured, their lives would have been saved and the injuries prevented, if they had kept up with air-bags the past twenty-five years. The system also is designed so that in a crash from 12 to 18 m.p.h. the air-bag inflates softer for the passenger and in a crash above 18 m.p.h. it inflates more firmly. That was intended to reduce the air-bag risk to children. That's a feature that was then abandoned and virtually all of the present air-bag systems do not have a safe feature to protect children.'

When Cole left GM so did the impetus for continuing to promote air-bags. As Ben Kelly explains, 'GM withdrew its air-bags from marketing about a year or two later, having sold only ten thousand of these and made only ten thousand.' Indeed, GM stopped fitting the bags even before the accompanying marketing campaign had been completed. Research proved that the corporation had also committed three errors: the dealers had remained unconvinced; buyers were still worried about the safety of the device; and it had been fitted on larger models instead of on the smaller vehicles on which it would have been more acceptable and useful.

After Cole left General Motors he contacted Ben Kelly and a colleague, 'and said that the car companies would never put in air-bags without government requirements, something that was heresy within the automotive industry. When Cole dropped out of the picture and it's one of those rare cases where one man does make a huge difference historically, basically whatever steam there had been in the air-bag progress within the industry died.'

This had one well-publicized ironic result. On 7 October 1975 sixty-two-year-old Dr Arnold Arms from Kansas walked away from a head-on collision with a bus, the first known case of an air-bag saving a life. But Dr

Arms was unable to replace his old car with a new one similarly equipped because Cole's successors had returned to their previous hard-line opposition to any restraints in line with a GM policy of opposing any federal interference in their business.

Meanwhile, the seat-belt cause was gaining ground. In the mid-1960s the Australian state of Victoria, the first authority in the world to adopt a law making the wearing of belts mandatory, reported that accident-related injuries had dropped by nearly a quarter in urban areas and by an eighth in the country. By the early 1970s Britain, too, was well on the way to insisting on the installation and wearing of belts.

GM tried an old trick: it produced misleading research 'proving' that seat-belts were hazardous. The requirement proposed by the NHTSA was frozen until Volvo came up a study involving 28,000 accidents without any deaths in impacts at under 60 m.p.h. in which drivers and passengers had worn shoulder harnesses, while unprotected drivers had been killed at speeds of as low as 12 m.p.h.

Cole's ideas had naturally provoked a reaction among other car manufacturers. Volkswagen, by now an important factor in the market, invested its money in a revolutionary automatic belt system. Ford's position was more complex. In December 1970 Henry Ford had appointed Lee Iacocca as President of Ford Motors. In the mid-1950s Iacocca, a self-described 'safety nut', had been one of McNamara's supporters in his ill-fated 'dash for safety' (although, ironically, he had made his name with the hazardous 'wild Mustang'). This experience had convinced him that only federal regulation would work. But he had his own solution to the problem of occupant protection: the 'interlock' system, an unwieldy safety harness connected to the ignition, so that the car could not be started unless the seat-belts of both front-seat occupants had been buckled. The idea was cheaper than the air-bag, was fully developed and could be installed more quickly. But the 'Iacocca Safety Belt' so irritated motorists that the idea lasted only a year and, indeed, turned the public against federally imposed safety requirements in general.

Until 1977 disagreements within the NHTSA did not help matters at a time when the economic effects of the oil crisis of 1973 had made change even more difficult. But the election of Jimmy Carter to the presidency in November 1976 transformed the situation. The following month William Coleman, the retiring Secretary of Transportation, concluded that passive restraints – both air-bags and automatic seat-belts – were feasible, but he stressed the importance of gaining public acceptance. The hostility that had built up against any federal regulations was best solved, he felt, through a large-scale demonstration programme involving 500,000 cars during the model years 1979 and 1980.

In safety matters, as in many other spheres, the Carter administration witnessed a mass of good intentions sabotaged by clumsy implementation and federal administrators not having enough clout to withstand pressure from the industry. Nevertheless by 1980 Carter's Secretary of Transportation, Brook Adams, had managed to ensure that all large cars produced after 1 September 1981 (the start of the 1982 model year) must have automatic restraints. However, interminable squabblings in Congress prevented any real progress, and the safety cause was not helped by Ralph Nader who, conforming to the principle that 'the best is the enemy of the good', helped sabotage more far-reaching legislation on the rather dodgy grounds that if a new administration tried to rescind Adams's plans the action would 'rekindle the consumer movement'.

If the pro-regulation Jimmy Carter could not get his way, then neither, it transpired, could his successor, Ronald Reagan, a firm and natural opponent of all forms of regulation. In his first speech on the subject, to the National Auto Dealers' Convention in early 1981, he declared that 'This administration opposes regulations.' As a sign of his determination he appointed as head of the NHTSA Raymond Peck, an actively anti-environmentalist lawyer. In November 1981, and against the advice of virtually all his officials, Peck revoked Carter's law imposing automatic restraints (i.e. those automatically triggered on impact), just as it was about to come into effect. Or, at least, he tried to, for by then the do-gooders had been joined by an even more powerful force, the insurance industry – and it was the powerful Allstate Insurance company which sued the NHTSA.

This represented a dramatic change: before Nader, the insurance companies had not exercised anything like the influence potentially at their disposal, given that they had detailed information on the damage caused by different types of vehicles in any given crash situation. They had been most unwilling to put their heads above the parapet. 'They don't want us telling them how to build autos,' said one insurer, 'and we don't want them telling us how to sell insurance.'

The general climate of deregulation in the 1980s meant that recalls of models found to have serious faults fell by nearly a third. The standard of manufacture was then so low that one out of every five cars sold was the subject of an NHTSA recall request with which the manufacturer refused to comply and the agency gave in – over such scandals as faulty transmissions on over twenty million Ford cars that jumped from Park to Reverse, which was responsible for five hundred deaths before Nader's Raiders finally secured a recall and redesign.

But the most adverse publicity was attracted by Ford's Pinto. Like its rival, the Corvair, it was a bright idea that went wrong, bringing a good deal of well-deserved abuse on its manufacturers. As John Telnack, the Ford designer, says, the Pinto was designed as an 'affordable, compact, five-seater, one again that looked sporty but was economical and met the needs of the time. The shape of it was new, it was fresh, it was the first three-door fast-back type of car that we'd done in this country. It was a different approach to design and people seemed to like it very much.' Even the name helped because, like the Mustang, people associated it with horses and the Wild West. In the early 1970s it soon became the best-selling sub-compact car in the US. But it had been rushed on to the market to combat the threat from Japanese imports and had a fatal flaw: rear-end collisions ruptured the fuel tank.

As Byron Bloch explains: 'The fuel tank is located very close to the rear bumper and in a rear impact it gets crushed against the rear axle, the tank gets punctured, ruptured, fuel is expelled, gets ignited, and infernos have burned up people over the years. Dozens and dozens of cases occurred when people were burned in Pinto rear-impact accidents. The fault really hit the public when one Richard Grimshaw sued Ford in a California court. Grimshaw was a passenger in a Pinto that was rear-ended, ironically by another Ford. In the accident his face was melted, his body was horribly burned and his fingers were melted also. It was a tragedy beyond belief. In the trial that took place, I had found various crucial Ford documents, one of which was a letter from the Ford Motor Company arguing why they should not make fuel-tank system improvements. They said that there will be 180 burn deaths per year at $200,000 value per burn death, there will be 180 serious burn injuries per year at $67,000 per serious burn injury, and there will also be thousands of burned vehicles and there was a value on that. When you added all those numbers together it came out to an annual benefit of around $50 million. Ford said we can fix the problem for $11 per vehicle but if you multiply the $11 per vehicle by the many millions of vehicles made per year, that came out to $150 million. So Ford was arguing it was cheaper to let 'em burn and it was that corporate attitude that convinced the jury to award $125 million in punitive damages as punishment to Ford Motor Company for that attitude of trading off human lives for a few dollars of profit. That letter revealed the inner thinking of car companies with regard to safety. To make matters worse, Ford had lobbied against a federal safety requirement that would have forced it to redesign the car.'

Dave Evans, the former GM designer, remembers how one owner rebelled by 'painting a target circle on the trunk with the gas tank on it. I'll never forget that.' But he also pinpoints the Pinto drama as 'the start of a new era where we had to be really careful about all the designs, every little thing about the car'.

But as John Telnack points out: 'There were a number of other cars, both domestic and imports, some of the Japanese cars, that actually had more serious fuel-tank problems than the Pinto, so I guess you could say a little of the reporting at the time was a little bit unbalanced.'

But the manufacturers still had the upper hand, as was shown when the government arranged for three Research Safety Vehicles (RSVs) to be built. The project manager, Jerry Kossar, claims that in his opinion the RSV 'was the safest car ever built. It was built to be attractive, economical and cheap to operate. It paid attention to real crashes and was designed to ameliorate the fatalities and injuries in these real-life crashes, not theoretical barrier crashes alone. Additionally it employed a structure which made it resist penetration of the passenger compartment in all modes of crash, frontal, side and rear, as well as roll-over. It also incorporated advanced air-bag systems which have since been shown to accommodate small children, out of position, standing right in front of the air-bag, as well as all size occupants. The industry snubbed this and that is part of the reason we now have such problems here in the United States with our air-bags.

'Generally their reaction was very negative. Although they admitted exceptional safety performance, they insisted that the RSV could not be produced in mass production. The auto industry historically makes evolutionary changes, small changes, in the design of cars, which are acceptable to their customers, whereas the RSV was new from the ground up. That was one complaint that they made, that they would not be able to sell such a vehicle. Secondly they could not produce such a vehicle because of the non-conventional structure which required filling with foam during construction and the emissions from this foam filling would require special treatment from the air system. Lastly – and this is very subjective on my part – there was another major reason why the manufacturers in the United States did not pick up on the RSV approach. That was their concern with product liability. No manufacturer could afford to change the production of all his model lines in the same year, and the remaining models would be looked at as unsafe and would subject him to liability claims in court cases where people were injured or killed and pointed to the safer model that he did make that year: why didn't he use it on my car?

'In the early 1990s fuel economy was a major issue in the United States. The auto industry maintained it would require smaller cars, lighter cars, which would not be safe and would cause higher fatalities and injuries. The presence of the research safety vehicle demonstrated that safer cars could be produced that were light and fuel efficient . . . So what happened next was that the remaining research safety vehicles were subjected to next to meaningless tests in crash which did not demonstrate their safety. These tests were shams in that test dummies were not even used in some tests, air-bags were not deployed. The fact that these tests took place caught me by surprise. I only learnt of them afterwards. After each test the cars would be shredded completely to demolish all evidence of their ever having existed.'

Despite their ruthless opposition to the RSVs, by the early 1980s American-based manufacturers had begun to understand that safety could be a weapon, not a threat. The breakthrough probably came with a study published by the IIHS showing that Japanese cars, which were posing an increasing threat to American-made vehicles, were the least safe of all the small cars on the market. GM promptly, and surprisingly, exploited the IIHS's findings in its sales campaigns.

While Allstate's suit was passing through the courts, Raymond Peck was trying to persuade manufacturers to adopt a voluntary programme to demonstrate the effectiveness of air-bags. In 1983 Mercedes-Benz stimulated the flagging safety campaign by announcing that driver's-side air-bags would be sold as an optional extra on some of their models, in addition to the lap- and shoulder-belt system fitted as standard equipment. Mercedes' policy was boosted by a well-publicized collision between one of its cars and a BMW, which was not equipped with an air-bag. The driver of the BMW was killed, while the driver of the Mercedes walked away from the accident virtually unscathed.

Mercedes' campaign helped to lead to the conversion of Lee Iacocca, by now the charismatic head of Chrysler. Accompanied by an ad campaign that asked 'Who says you can't teach an old dog new tricks?' he had all new Chryslers fitted with air-bags. At that point in 1990 GM gave in, but the six-year delay, from 1984 when the Carter proposals would have come into effect to when GM surrendered, is estimated to have cost up to 60,000 lives – although such estimates tend to have been plucked out of thin air rather than based on any serious statistical analysis.

Market forces had worked, albeit belatedly. The public wanted greater safety; the industry responded (as we shall see later). The figures* showed the change: between 1972 and 1987 those favouring fines for not wearing a seat-belt rose from 23 to 54 per cent of respondents; the percentage of children observed travelling unrestrained fell from 83 per cent in 1979 to 15 per cent in 1986, and the use of seat-belts rose from 28 to 69 per cent in the same period. Typically, the usage rate soared in the first few months after legislation came into force, then retreated, but only to a level up to three times larger than the previous rate, ensuring that injuries were reduced by up to a fifth.

In late 1982 the US Supreme Court agreed to review Peck's decision not to implement the law on automatic restraints, although a local court in Washington had overturned a previous judicial decision that restraints be fitted. The following June it surprised onlookers – and the industry, which at this stage was still hoping that Peck's ruling would remain in force – by stating that it had been unlawful. Justice Byron White said that Peck's decision had been 'arbitrary and capricious' and that the manufacturers had waged 'the equivalent of war against air-bags and lost'.

*See *Autosafety* by John Graham.

The Supreme Court's ruling was a major milestone in the tangled story of car safety, and must have had a considerable psychological effect on the manufacturers: they had understood that they faced an unprecedentedly powerful combination of the economic might of the insurance industry and the Supreme Court, which commands a much greater degree of respect in the United States than politicians or bureaucrats and created a politically respectable umbrella under which the opposing parties could reach agreement.

By the mid-1980s, the public's mood had also changed decisively in favour of federal intervention. Roger Smith, one of the few chairmen of GM who had never run an auto division,* was unable to persuade Elizabeth Dole, Reagan's new Secretary for Transportation, to try to overturn the Supreme Court's decision. At the same time GM's economic clout was weakening as the company's market share slid to around 20 per cent, a far cry from the days, only thirty years earlier, when its 50 per cent share had enabled it to stifle any opposition and prevent Ford from boasting of safety improvements.

In July 1984 Dole announced a phased programme to ensure that by 1990 every new car sold was fitted with automatic restraints (i.e. air-bags), and encouraged individual states to adopt mandatory seat-belt laws. If two-thirds of the population was covered by such laws within five years, then – and only then – would there be no legal requirement to fit air-bags. This stirred the industry, led by GM, into creating an organization called Traffic Safety Now, designed to promote the compulsory use of seat-belts.

Meanwhile, Nader had persuaded the General Services Administration (GSA), the purchasing organization for the US government, to insist on air-bags for government vehicles. Chrysler and GM refused to bid for the contract, but Ford did, and in 1985 delivered 53,000 cars with air-bags, which showed just how far the company had changed since the retirement of Henry Ford II in 1979. It also demonstrated that, in the US, competition extends beyond business to the government itself, for the GSA was also a pioneer in insisting on the installation of advanced safety glass. In this way Nader used the inter-agency 'turf wars' so normal in Washington to bypass the Department of Transportation's relatively leisurely programme.

Henry Ford's retirement had enabled the company to look at safety in a new and more positive light, especially as research showed clearly that car buyers now listed it as one of their major priorities. Soon the company was offering driver's-side air-bags as standard equipment. Ford was also able to reduce the cost of fitting air-bags since a ruling by the head of the NHTSA

---

*Smith will probably be best remembered for his absence from Michael Moore's film *Roger and Me* (and, by implication, for his refusal to confront Moore), about how GM turned the city of Flint to a job-free zone by shutting all its factories in the city.

that fitting automatic protection to both occupants of the front seat would count as an additional credit when working out whether Ford had fulfilled the quota system introduced by Dole that forced manufacturers to fit safety features to at least some of their cars.

Nevertheless the public remained reluctant to spend any additional money on having air-bags fitted, even though insurers offered reduced premiums if cars were fitted with them. Ford tried to change the rules: it promised to equip all its cars with automatic seat-belts from the 1990 model year on, as the law provided, but it would confine air-bags to the driver's side, a proposal that, of course, infuriated campaigners: 'They want to protect the driver but not the passenger,' declared Clarence Ditlow, head of Nader's Center for Automobile Safety, though Nader himself remained silent. But Dole agreed to delay the provision of full automatic front-seat protection for another four years for cars that had driver's-side protection

By the late 1980s safety was an idea whose time had, finally, come. And, as John Graham points out, the delay in introducing air-bags was not entirely negative for those who had doubted Ed Cole's claims to have produced a satisfactory one. As he points out: 'If the relatively primitive, untested air-bag systems of the early 1970s had been installed on an industry-wide basis, adverse public reactions might have led to premature rejection of the technology. Industry opposition bought precious time for early air-bag systems to be tested, refined, and transformed into commercially acceptable products.' The only major regret was that the officials at the NHTSA had not tried harder in the 1970s to promote the compulsory wearing of seat-belts. But, then, they were bureaucrats and not, like Nader, persuaders.

Despite the undoubted advances, the battle continues. The manufacturers are still unwilling to acknowledge all the defects in their cars – and not only because they want to keep their image bright and shiny but also because their customers are looking for the slightest opportunity to sue such rich and powerful organizations. In their warranties manufacturers tell their dealers – but not the general public – about faults. They allow the dealers to claim compensation for rectifying any defects not by admitting their existence but by using phrases like 'policy adjustments', 'good-will programs' or 'extended warranties' to cover the repayments.

Today Ben Kelly still takes the example of air-bags to show the manufacturers' inadequacies. He complains that they were kept out of cars for too long, and that the manufacturers spent too much time and effort fighting the US government rather than improving their design. But how far it is fair to blame today's managers for the sins of their predecessors is another matter.

4

Mrs Castle's Crusade

In general, the pattern of events in Britain did not echo that in the United States. The passion for the car as symbol was less strong, the motor industry less formidable, ruthless or, indeed, hostile. The first awareness of safety as an issue came in the 1950s and effective action in the mid-1960s. And although the impetus for change in both countries came from a single individual the two personalities concerned could not have been more different. In the United States Ralph Nader was a lonely young lawyer without any apparent political clout; in Britain Barbara Castle was a powerful cabinet minister – which is not to say that her task was easy, just that she was able to carry through her proposals more quickly and decisively than could Nader.

However, in the 1950s and 1960s there were echoes in the British motor industry of the atmosphere in the United States. When the future Lord Lucas joined his family car dealership the austerities of the 1940s and early 1950s had vanished. 'Here was a great release. People could make a free choice and this was the expression of freedom. They could go where they wanted, when they wanted, they'd come into a showroom. I think they liked the amount of chrome that was on motor-cars. The ladies particularly liked the colour schemes, the interiors were important. Radios, of course, were not standard equipment any more than a heater was or windscreen washers, so we sold them that, that's what they wanted to buy. They wanted to buy a piece of freedom, a piece of luxury. This was a big purchase for young people, and particularly young couples, more important to them then than a house. They wanted this freedom and they didn't want rules and restrictions and things like that encumbering them – this was a curtailment of their great enjoyment. The car was their expression of freedom. They weren't concerned with safety – or even with the technical aspects of the purchase. I remember, as a salesman in a showroom, if a client wanted the bonnet to be lifted up we thought, Oh, my God, he knows more about it than we do, dear oh dear, what are we going to do now? Let's get them in the car and give them a trial.'

The veteran accident and emergency specialist Dr Howard Baderman was one of those who saw the other side of the new-found freedom. He remembers that 'In the fifties when I was a student and newly qualified, accident departments were dealing with ordinary injuries and illnesses, cuts and bruises and falls and people injuring themselves at work and so forth, and road traffic accidents were relatively infrequent. Then in the late part of the fifties and the early sixties we became aware quite rapidly, although it seemed to creep up on us, that road accidents were really a very major part of our work.'

To Baderman, and others like him, it was 'extraordinary for society not to realize the minefield it was creating for itself with new developments such as the widespread use of cars, until as the years went by the carnage developed. It ought to be predictable and we ought to be able to act earlier – there's the seeming impossibility of getting anything done about it. The car became not just a status symbol but essential and really rather precious, and there were a large number of them and you couldn't do anything, really, in terms of modifying their design or bringing in protective measures to minimize the totally predictable trauma. All sorts of organizations, civil liberties organizations, road organizations and so forth, were dead against doing anything that would somehow interfere with the pleasure and the necessity of the car, whatever the trauma it was causing, and it was really a very uphill struggle to get something done about it.'

One of the first researchers to respond to doctors' pleas was Professor Murray Mackay, Britain's first automobile accident investigator. He started his work in 1964 'when accidents were viewed almost entirely in terms of preventing them by better education, better driver training. People were getting killed and seriously injured in really low-speed accidents and I became interested in how they got hurt. I wasn't interested in the cause of the accident, I was interested in the injuries and the design of the car, and this was a subject that didn't interest the manufacturers at all, they weren't focused on that. The whole emphasis at the time was the nut behind the wheel, how to change driving, how to prevent accidents in the first place. The idea of crash performance was a very new idea at that time.

'I've always been interested in cars, and I'm trained as a mechanical engineer. Both of my parents were doctors so I grew up in a house where the human body and injuries was an everyday dinner-table conversation, so the two came together in a sense and that's how I got interested in the biomechanics of injuries – the link between vehicle design and structure and the injuries that result in car crashes. When I first got started the basic ways that people knew about accidents came from police reports and from insurance-company records, and I thought it would be a good way to do research, to actually go and look at crashes. That was a new idea at the time so I recruited a surgeon, a psychologist and a highway engineer, and I was a vehicle engineer. We looked at accidents in a very broad-brush comprehensive way, involving all those four disciplines. This was a very fruitful way to get new knowledge about crashes and their causes and, in particular, to learn about the consequences in terms of vehicle design and injuries. We went to the scenes of crashes within thirty minutes or so of their occurrence and collected information, photographed everything we could see, measured the scenes and developed detailed crash-investigation techniques.

'I learnt a lot by following some of the big crash investigations that were done on air crashes in Britain. I spent time with the Accident Investigation Board, rebuilding aircraft and learning about how you analyse structures, how you look for contact between occupants and structures and so on.' In particular, he looked at the crash of an Argosy aircraft at Manchester airport. His team was not the only one: 'There were other people around the world – there was a team in the United States, a team in Australia, some people in Sweden were doing work, so there were several of us who began to look at crashes from this point of view at the same time.

'In 1960s car design, there were all sorts of things wrong with the interior. For example, the supports for the rear-view mirror were little die-cast shafts that were very hostile, the steering column was a solid shaft going right the way forward to the steering box so in a frontal crash it would be driven backwards and take the driver's chest and face directly rearwards into the steering wheel, the instrument panels were often die-cast materials, windshields were made out of toughened glass so that when it broke you got a row of fragments in the bottom edge. We saw lots of people losing their eyesight on those last rows of glass fragments. Door latches were opening in very low-speed simple accidents, and people were being thrown out and injured or dying, landing on the road surface, so there were a host of things that were very, very wrong.

'Once you become sensitive to how people get hurt then you see all sorts of ways in which you could improve things, particularly at that time, because crash performance wasn't part of the design process. The people designing cars were basically saying that if you have a crash it's your own fault and you're on your own. The new ideas that were just developing in the mid-sixties were saying, Well, that's really not good enough. What we should do is learn from experience in aircraft design, take those ideas into the design of cars and admit that people are going to go on having crashes and do something about minimizing the injuries that result.

'The doctors were beginning to realize that people were dying after their vehicle had been involved in an accident at speeds as low as 10 m.p.h., that most of the patients they were treating were victims of car accidents and most of them had identical injuries from hitting the windshield or steering wheel, that steering wheels crushed chests, that radio knobs penetrated skulls and doors sprang open spilling bodies on to the concrete. But, as Baderman says, 'People just took it for granted that accidents happened, and when they saw one they said, "There but for the grace of God go I," and nobody imagined that there was anything that could be done about it.' Researchers, like Mackay, could 'see that people were dying and being injured by features in the design of the cars that could easily be changed. And yet there was still great reluctance from the manufacturers. Talk of safety and accident was anathema . . . but cars killed . . . knobs, steering columns, windshields, door handles' – and any other protruding features.

None of this concerned contemporary car designers, who did not concern themselves with the *second* collision, between the occupants and the car's interior, or between a pedestrian or cyclist and its exterior. The king of this school was Alec Issigonis, the towering genius who designed the Mini, a man uninterested in anything except the manoeuvrability of his cars and confirmed in his beliefs by the way in which the Morris Minor, the Mini and, later, the Morris 1100, sold in their millions. He was uninterested in style or even in a comfortable driving position – he himself drove hunched over the steering wheel which he always set as vertical as possible.

The Mini was a stupendous achievement. It had been rushed into production in a mere two years after Issigonis had been given the brief to design a car as small as possible that would have 'four wheels, four seats and four cylinders' in response to the tiny Bubble cars that enjoyed temporary popularity after the Suez crisis of 1956. Issigonis believed that the undoubtedly superior handling qualities of the Mini would enable drivers to 'drive their way out of danger . . . steer clear of accidents', although it also encouraged millions of ordinary motorists to drive far faster than they had ever dreamed possible because it seemed so much safer to drive, due to its superb handling and stability on the road, than any previous small car.

Today Issigonis's philosophy is explained by Jack Daniels, who was in charge of the mechanical elements of the Mini under Issigonis's firm direction. He claims: 'Safety in the car was on my mind from the very handling of the vehicle, to be able to avoid the accident instead of going into it.' He staunchly defends the Mini: 'I think it's a safe car. Unquestionably the dexterity of that car is the bit that you can't evaluate, you can't get a number on it, but it's a thing which is there – the sheer ability to miss an accident is there.' Indeed, the Mini *was* far more manoeuvrable than any small car before or since.

To Murray Mackay, though, the Mini was a nightmare in a second collision. The filler cap stuck out: if the car rolled over, 'the filler cap gets sheared off, you've got fuel pouring out, you've got an electrical source and you've got a big fire immediately. The door latch is just like an ordinary house latch so if the door gets stretched, the frame gets stretched, then the door will just open out and people will be ejected and fall out without any resistance at all. You've got seats which just hinge at the front so in a crash with somebody at the back they've got nothing to stop on until they hit the people in the front. You've got a really short nose on this little car so there's no crush space. The engine comes back against the far wall and then the whole lot comes forward into the interior of the vehicle. So we said some very unpleasant things about the Mini in the local newspapers and I got a summons to go to Longbridge [the factory in Birmingham where Issigonis worked] to talk to Alec Issigonis.

'He put me on the carpet in front of his desk and after an exchange, he basically said to me, "You know, young man, I make my cars with such good brakes, such good steering, that if people get into a crash it's their own fault." We had what you might call a spirited exchange of views because I thought this was a stupid approach to take, and very old-fashioned, and told him so and wrote as much in the local papers. Then time passed, and we cooled down but the Mini was a failure in North America. It was withdrawn because it couldn't meet even the safety regulations at that time.'

Today, Daniels is prepared to acknowledge the importance of the second collision as he recounts the story of the Mini's first recorded accident. Stirling Moss, then Britain's best-known racing driver, had a crash while driving a prototype. He escaped unharmed and 'his wife got out with just a cut on her forehead from the visor and that's all we heard of it until we got the car back. Now, I kicked myself when we got the car back because the steering wheel had gone forward, pushed the screen out, and still remained circular. Everybody was talking about safety steering columns and I thought, Christ, we've got a safety steering column, hadn't even thought about it, but there it was and as it had been out for public inspection I couldn't patent it. Afterwards I had to go to a number of colleges and talk about the Mini. Every time I did, I mentioned this steering wheel and, invariably someone would get up from the back and say, "That's right, that happened to me just like that." It's one of the safety elements of the car but we can't claim we intended it because we didn't know it was there!'

Issigonis's attitude towards safety brought him into conflict, not only with researchers like Mackay, but with the most remarkable Minister of Transport in the history of the job: the tough, gutsy, glamorous red-haired Barbara Castle. When she was appointed in March 1965 she inherited from her predecessor, Tom Fraser, a government White Paper that dealt with drunk drivers and faulty goods vehicles. She recorded in her memoirs:

In my legislation I stuck closely to the White Paper with two modifications. First I decided that random checks would be less effective than giving the police the right to breath-test on suspicion of the driver having alcohol in the body or on committal of a moving traffic offence. Secondly I tightened up on the penalties for driving above the drink limit, providing for automatic disqualification from driving for twelve months on conviction of the offence. The bill became law in May 1967. I received a record post-bag, half praise, half abuse.

Later that year she went further with a much more wide-ranging White Paper on road safety, which, combined with her own popularity, was widely welcomed and enabled her to carry through the first thorough-going reform of road safety since 1934.

When she became minister she found that people were resigned to the risks of the road, but the research she saw from the Road Research Laboratory impressed her and persuaded her that it was possible to identify and isolate the causes of certain accidents and then deal with them. 'What worried me at the time was that the mounting casualties on the roads threatened to rise and rise. To me it was intolerable that any minister would stand back and allow this dreadful carnage to go on without attempting to reduce it.

'It was, of course, a very dangerous road to become the first ever woman Minister of Transport because to most men the car is a virility symbol, and to have a woman come along and tell them they mustn't drive as fast or they can't drink and drive or they must wear a seat-belt was wholly unacceptable. I used to get angry, almost life-threatening letters from indignant men who would sign themselves "Three Old Regulars" or something like that. They deeply resented, to begin with at any rate, having a woman Minister of Transport, particularly as that woman did not drive herself. They couldn't accept that there was such a thing as an objective view of how drivers should behave on the roads because they weren't being objective. They were having a love affair with their cars, and the bigger and more beautiful the car the better. Safety was a sideline for them in that period, so it was difficult to come along with quite demanding reforms.

'It took time and the motoring organizations fought me, my own ministry was not very enthusiastic. It was a very macho institution and the ministerial floor didn't even have a woman's lavatory. It was a man's world, you see, and in I walk with these ideas that speed kills, that seat-belts can save one from injury, that there is no human right to drink and drive. Interfering with the "human right" to drink and drive was saving someone else's life that might have been lost by a driver's thoughtlessness.' She didn't even get whole-hearted support from her ministerial colleagues for all her proposals. 'I remember Roy Jenkins, for instance, who was then Chancellor of the Exchequer, very indignant at my seventy-mile-an-hour speed limit on motorways. He liked to do a bit of speeding himself.'

But she loved the job 'more than any other job I ever did because you could combine a feeling of compassion for the people whom you were trying to help with a hard realism. You know, get the facts and then you've got the job of convincing people that the facts show that the measures you're taking are going to help them. A slow business – but it worked.'

To convince people, especially men, she used her unique combination of wit and feminine charm. The going could be tough: 'Some of the most macho people in the argument were the motoring organizations. Before I came on the scene there'd been an absolute assumption that motoring was a man's world. It would tolerate women drivers while laughing at them. I remember being invited by one of the big motoring organizations to speak at one of their lunches. They were overwhelmed by their own daring because they kept saying to me, "You know, we've never had a woman minister before," so when I came to speak, I always used to make myself look as nice as I could, sailed in, smiled at everybody, very feminine, but when it came to making my speech, I would begin by saying, "I understand that I'm the first woman ever to be invited to one of your lunches. Well, the ratio of one woman to two hundred men is about right," and, of course, they had to laugh and if you can get people laughing and realizing you're not an ogre or a nanny or a headmistress, you're a woman in a job that affects women just as much as it does men, and that you're going to bring to bear a woman's softnesses as well as toughnesses, then you can win.'

Her programme was summed up in the title of her White Paper, 'Road Safety, A Fresh Approach'. But she knew that budgets were tight and had to ensure, as she says, 'that you're getting the maximum value for every pound you spend, value in terms of lives saved or injuries reduced. I appointed an economic planning unit who used to do me these cost-benefit analyses of different forms of proposals for reducing accidents, and it emerged from that that it wasn't necessarily the most expensive ones that were the most effective.' For instance, one of her units 'did a marvellous job analysing local accidents, their causes and where they took place, and I used to go and visit them and it was an eye-opener. I found on one particularly dangerous stretch of road into Birmingham, which had a heavy accident record, that the bulk of the accidents took place at intersections, because you could say, "Slow", or whatever you liked on the side roads, but people will, you know, make a dash for it. It was relatively simple to make No Entry roads opposite and make people turn in, go slow and out again.'

Her most well-publicized battle was to carry through tough measures to combat drink-driving. The battle could be said to have started in 1953 when the Pedestrians' Association persuaded the Ministry of Transport to commission an anti-drinking poster from the Royal Society for the Prevention of Accidents (RoSPA) with the slogan 'One for the road may be one for the grave.' This created a rumpus, because the ministry shied away from endorsing the message on the poster. However, Castle's proposals to institute breath-testing were greatly boosted by a television programme, *This Week*, which intercut between the Birmingham Accident Hospital and drunks coming out of a pub on New Year's Eve explaining that they were all in favour of drink-driving restrictions but were themselves ('hic') perfectly fit to drive.

But Castle's biggest battle, comparable to the one in the United States over air-bags, was over seat-belts. When her ministry's experts realized that road safety was going to be one of her major preoccupations they produced all the evidence she needed from Australia where it had been established without any doubt that the wearing of seat-belts reduced serious or fatal casualties. She compared the expense of building roads with the introduction of seat-belts. 'For a modest sum, which incidentally adds nothing to public spending, the statistics showed that the return, in the form of reduced deaths and serious injuries, was the most effective of them all. I naturally pursued this because it seemed so simple. Here was a relatively inexpensive step which could save hundreds of lives and serious injuries.'

Lap-belts dated back to the early days of motoring – indeed, King Edward VII is pictured wearing one in a 1902 photo – and they had been fitted in aeroplanes well before they became standard in cars. The modern three-point belt was invented by two Swedes, Nils Bohlin and Bertil Aldman, and the first one installed in a Volvo in 1959.

Barbara Castle naturally claims the credit for seat-belt legislation, but the pioneer road-safety campaigner, Dr Howard Baderman, vividly remembers the battle: 'All sorts of stratagems were employed by the opponents of seat-belt legislation, civil liberties, unnecessary law, the British don't like too many laws that impinge on the individual. We were quite clear, there was irrefutable scientific and statistical evidence, that it would make a difference and the way we won that battle eventually was by a remarkable coincidence. There's a rather curious English custom when individual Members of Parliament put their names in a ballot to introduce their own Bill, and the only chance they get of that going on to the statute book is if they're in the first three of the ballot. An MP whose pet subject had been rendered useless by the ballot was desperate to find another subject. We met him at a cocktail party and said, "We've got just the subject for you. Why don't you put together a Bill to make seat-belt wearing by children compulsory?"

'He clutched at this with open arms. We had a frenzied two or three weeks, which was very enjoyable, in and out of the Houses of Parliament, lobbying MPs of all political persuasions, and we mobilized all the resources that we'd got from doctors and nurses and others who'd been slaving away for years with adult seat-belt legislation to no avail. The proposal was clearly unanswerable, it couldn't be opposed, and indeed the government of the day took over that Bill, which meant it was guaranteed to be passed into law.

It didn't have to fight on the House of Commons floor, as we put it, like other legislation did. Within a year or so of seat-belt legislation for children in the front seat of cars, which of course reduced the accidents to children very dramatically, there was little or no opposition to seat-belt laws for adults in front seats of cars.'

Baderman underestimates the depth of the opposition: until 1966 it was thought that the risk of serious injury was reduced by being thrown clear of the vehicle. That year, however, two researchers showed that ejection was the cause of a quarter of all road deaths, and would be almost eliminated by wearing a belt.

Yet as Castle herself recalls, seat-belts 'were looked upon as one of Barbara's nannyish gestures, and the danger I ran into was of being labelled as a representative of the nanny state, wanting to interfere in everybody's freedom of action, but I knew that one man's freedom in action would be another man's pain, or perhaps death, so I stuck at it. One of my most vociferous critics over the seat-belt issue was Harold Lever, financial secretary of the Treasury, a wonderful chap, I was very fond of Harold, a lively, spirited and wealthy man. He was once driving me back from a meeting we'd been at together and he said to me, "Barbara, you've got a convert. The son of a dear friend of mine will be in a wheelchair for life because he was driving his car, not at any great speed and another car crashed into him and hurled him through the windscreen. He couldn't deny that if the boy had been wearing a seat-belt his injury would have been minimal." That, I think, is what eventually convinced people.

'Another great source of resistance was the women government drivers, wonderful bunch of women, very good drivers who used to take ministers around the place in their ministerial cars. I was good friends with mine but, oh dear, she did disapprove of the attempt to make the wearing of seat-belts compulsory because she was a rather large-bosomed woman, you see, and she used to say it cut into her bosom!

'Others used to argue, "Oh, there's no proof that wearing a seat-belt won't so restrict the driver as to cause more accidents or as many as," but it was a question of getting people to cut through the romance of their relationship with the car, to face the reality that they could go home from a day out or a day's work injured for life or even a corpse.'

She is, perhaps, unfair to her opponents, whose reactions were not entirely emotional. As Lord Lucas, a veteran of the motor business points out, in the mid-1960s 'The belts that were available *were* very restrictive. Little work was being done to make them more user-friendly and then, of course, there was a lot of anecdotal evidence that if you were strapped into this tin box in a restrictive belt in which you couldn't move, you were likely to be more seriously injured.

'Anecdotal evidence is not good evidence but some years before seat-belts were introduced I was involved in an accident. I actually drove a motor-car underneath a trailer. It stopped when I hit the rear axle, by which time two-thirds of the roof had been taken off and the steering wheel was bent over but it so happened that it was at a comparatively low speed and I lay down and it all passed over my head. Had I been wearing a seat-belt I would have been decapitated. At that time there were other anecdotal stories of this nature, so it did make us pretty suspicious about what we were being asked to strap ourselves in with.'

Fortunately for Castle, and other supporters of seat-belts, 'The civil liberties issue which some Members of Parliament tried to raise in the House of Commons was not shared by the public at large, or certainly not by women drivers or women passengers. It was certainly felt very strongly by a few macho men who wanted to be free to do whatever they liked – they'd paid the road tax – on the road and with their own car. It was an uphill struggle but it was amazing to me how quickly people adapted to it.'

She was clever in using a well-loved and familiar figure, Jimmy Savile, then a disc jockey, to launch the campaign 'to help me sell the idea that it was just as natural as opening a car door to put on a seat-belt once you were inside. We did great sort of photography larks, expeditions with him while he was selling this "clunk-click, every trip" slogan. Coming from Jimmy, it didn't look so much of a nannyish thing, but just a good-natured natural thing to do, and today, I think, most people feel undressed unless they've got their seat-belt on in a car. I find it's rather amusing because if I'm in a train I'm looking for my seat-belt – it's so automatic to strap oneself in.'

Nevertheless she had to adopt a 'softly softly' approach because the chassis of most cars then on the road was not strong enough to cope with the force of a seat-belt holding in a human being – itself, as she says, 'a terrible commentary on the nature of car construction'. However, the lack of strength that the seat-belt issue revealed in the fundamental structure of their vehicles shocked the car industry and led them to ponder the contribution the structure of a car could make in improving road safety.

The installation of belts required a lot of thinking on the part of the manufacturers. As Jeff Crandall explains: 'To design the ideal seat-belt you have to study the movement of bodies inside cars and the transfer of the energy produced in a collision. [You need] to distribute that in the best possible way and that means distributing it to the strongest possible structures. For example, a shoulder-belt tries to deliver the force to the upper shoulder, which is a fairly strong complex, rather than concentrating it, say, in the abdomen. That's why they've gone with a three-point belt as opposed to just the lap-belt. You need to understand how the forces are going to be distributed, what the occupant might interact with, where they might contact in the vehicle, and then you mitigate that by using padding or seat-belts or air-bags to minimize the risk of injury to those regions that would come in contact with the vehicle interior.'

Castle proceeded cautiously. 'I had to begin by making the fitting of seat-belts compulsory in all new cars and in cars put on the road since 1965, two years earlier. I watched a lot of tests at the British Standards lab and at the Road Research Laboratory on different types of seat-belt to reassure people they were not being compelled by law to spend money on fitting something that could actually endanger their lives. Now, until every car was fitted with a seat-belt one could not enforce the wearing of them so that came later. By then we [Labour] were out of office and I was no longer a minister, but as a back-bench MP I always voted for making the wearing of seat-belts compulsory because that had been my ultimate goal when I started on the same road as Australia.'

Barbara Castle's legacy lay not only in the laws and regulations she pushed through but, more importantly, in the transformed attitude towards driving among the general public, a new-found concern with safety, a momentum that has never failed. At the end of the 1960s the motoring correspondent of the *Sunday Times* was Judith Jackson. She had two children and was concerned for their safety in cars. She found that many of the special seats then available for children were hopelessly inadequate, to the point of being dangerous, so she campaigned week in and week out, for proper standards, and had her way. Standards were imposed, children's lives were saved. You could attribute her success to a number of factors, including her strong-minded personality, journalistic skills and the willingness of the then editor, Harold Evans, to back her. But at the root was the fact that Barbara Castle had made road safety a legitimate and public issue.

Castle's work provided that new cars were fitted with seat-belts. It took a further fifteen years to ensure that drivers and front-seat passengers were obliged to wear them, a law that had to overcome tremendous opposition. Lord Lucas exlains: 'Those of us who opposed the Bills were not opposed to seat-belts *per se*. We were opposed to compulsion because this was going to make criminals of people who felt that they had the right to make their own decisions about cars, safety measures, how they drove and so on. It took a long time to introduce inertia seat-belts where there was a degree of movement.' Until then, he says, 'There were problems health-wise for those who were short or fat, or large in other ways, pregnant women. Many were thought to be at some risk, and we didn't seem to have got right the exemptions from wearing them. In 1977 two Bills were introduced into Parliament, the first was lost by two or three votes and then Lord Wigg introduced another similar Bill, which was lost by a handsome majority. I suppose by that time improvements had been made, and there was evidence from Australia of huge life savings. The climate of opinion was beginning to change: the idea that the Englishman had a right to drive his motor-car wherever, whenever, however he pleased, was fading.'

What changed Lord Lucas's mind was a trip to Australia, where he got into the habit of wearing a seat-belt, and found that 'This wasn't such a terrible thing. It was not as restrictive as one might have thought. By the time I got back home the legislation was moving in 1982 towards compulsion. In the House of Lords the former resistance was wavering. I dropped my opposition and went along with the majority and in 1983 it became compulsory.' And, as he says, while seat-belts may not have been the prime reason for the reduction in deaths and injuries, none the less 'perhaps it was the measure that sparked off all the others, that made us more conscious about road safety'.

The British proved astonishingly law-abiding. Within two months of the law being passed the rate of belt-wearing had jumped from under 40 per cent – barely more than it had been a decade earlier – to well over 90 per cent, and there it has remained, although when it comes to rear seat-belts, which have been fitted as standard in all cars made since 1987 only children have been induced to wear them: 87 per cent of the under-fours wear one, a rate that drops dramatically to only two in five teenagers.

But some remain defiant. As far as Jack Daniels is concerned, 'In terms of safety . . . well, they [seat-belts] only go as far as the regulations demand. The last job I had when I was in the factory there was to have a go at even further safety for the Mini.' They were trying to make all cars, including the Mini, strong enough to absorb shocks of up to 40 m.p.h. 'We got the Mini up to about 38 miles per hour, which is something like 80 per cent stiffer than it was before. Now it costs you to do it. When you start asking for that you pay. And the cheapest thing is to miss the bloody accident in the first place.'

TODAY

5

The New Breeds
The Detectives: the Golden Hour

There's no such thing as an accident. There's always something. And,
no matter how small and seemingly insignificant, we've got to find it.
And when we do, then we can tell you exactly what happened.

Police Constable Mike Doyle

The everyday journey that turns into a disaster is the stuff of everyone's
worst nightmares. But sense can be made of the events leading up to every
such catastrophe. That is the work of the new breed of 'car-crash
detectives', teams of doctors and policemen who rush to the scene of an
accident to look at the crash environment. Their work is based on that of
the 'air-crash detectives', for car-safety experts copied the techniques used
by the 'tin-kickers' who investigate air crashes. Where previously they had
to rely on examining the victims as they arrived at hospital or the cars when
they arrived at the wreckers' yard, now they are at the crash site within
minutes to stop the evidence being moved so that they can piece together
the circumstances leading to the crash.

The only problem, certainly so far as Britain is concerned, is that it is too
expensive to keep professional crews on standby. As a result, the families of
the victims of road crashes often face lengthy, agonizing delays in their wait
for conclusive evidence as to the cause of a crash – and, of course, if the
evidence, the bodies and the wreckage, has been moved before the
'detectives' have done their work, then it has, in effect, been tampered with.
That this is accepted as inevitable provides proof that we are not yet
thinking of car crashes as crimes rather than as 'accidents'.

Nevertheless the detectives' work is proving vital in reducing the death
toll from crashes. According to Anthony Bleetman, an accident and
emergency consultant at Heartlands Hospital in Birmingham, there are
three periods during which accident victims die: immediately; within hours
– sometimes because the wrong treatment was given at the scene; and over

the following few weeks. According to Bleetman, the numbers in the first two categories have fallen, thanks partly to the detectives' work, above all in the first sixty minutes after the crash, the so-called 'Golden Hour'.

Bleetman is also a part-time member of BASICS, the British Association for Immediate Care, founded twenty years ago and now operating country-wide. It emerged, he says, that 'Once people had realized that doctors could be vital for treatment when patients are entrapped in road-traffic accidents and if there is a prolonged on-scene time for the fire service to extract them from the vehicle and load them on to the ambulance, there may be bleeding, an airway problem, or the victim may need anaesthesia at the scene and these are skills that are beyond normal paramedic skills.' However, BASICS is a voluntary service, without any substantial government funding.

The crash detective has been with us for some time. In the early 1960s, Don Huelke of the University of Michigan started studying crashes – although at the time, as he emphasizes, everyone assumed that the fault inevitably lay with the driver. In Britain, as we saw in the previous chapter, Murray Mackay had started to apply air-crash detective standards to road crashes. But he soon grasped the differences, and highlighted them in a report of 1970 in the *Journal of the Forensic Science Society*, namely that: 'Air crashes are infrequent, and on the whole very expensive in terms both of lives and of airframes, whereas road accidents are in many ways a statistical problem where remedial measures are discovered by the detection of recurring factors in many accidents which influence the occurrence of those events and their consequent injuries.'

Contrary to received opinion, Mackay found that there were a number of causes which accounted for accidents; the driver was involved in most cases, the other causes being the car itself, the environment or the prevailing conditions – indeed, one of the early findings of his research was the division of responsibility between these latter three factors. The result was that traffic engineers thought about improvements. As Mackay says, 'If you had put up street lighting then saw a 30 per cent reduction in night-time accidents, you had something useful.'

Since then a new type of forensic medicine has emerged, involving doctors, paramedics, the police and the fire service. These teams are trying simultaneously to rescue the victims; to give them medical assistance, whether they are still trapped, or at the scene but out of the car, or in hospital; to seek for the clues which will tell the doctors what injuries to look out for; and to provide the detectives with clues as to the cause of the accident, and how a similar one can be prevented in the future.

Immediate first aid is provided by paramedics attached to the fire service. As Malcolm Westwood, a fire-fighter, points out: 'Probably more people in this country are rescued by the fire service in road-traffic accidents than in fires so we really have a professional role where we're going to act as part of a team, we're going to look after the people.' Once they arrive on the scene 'there's quite a few rules that are attached to actually protecting people. We need to make sure that people are protected from shock or loss of blood and, of course, breathing difficulties. All of those need to be taken into account and obviously moving the casualty may have a distinct effect. Spinal injuries, broken bones and damaged limbs all have to be considered. It's no good just dragging people away. We're talking about moving the car away from the casualty.'

Westwood has twenty years' experience and in that time, he says, 'We've seen the role of the fire-fighters change quite dramatically. We're now talking about a team effort to rescue people. Whereas years ago we'd have perhaps taken the person from the car, we're now doing something fundamentally different, we're taking the car from the person. Now, that's not just cutting up cars for the sheer hell of it, this is actually part of a strategic approach to give the person the maximum time. The "Golden Hour" is a crucial element of that and that's where we're protecting people. We're saying, "We have to do this within this hour, and it's part of the review, it's part of the team effort and it's part of the ground rules for the whole operation." '

The Golden Hour figures large in all planning for accidents. The Free University of Berlin has provided the city with a Mobile Intensive Care Unit (MICU). 'We drive this car to severe road accidents,' says Dr Stefan Schmidt, an accident and emergency specialist, 'and we've got all the equipment for that. We've got an ECG for monitoring the heart-rate and we've got a bed to transport people and to monitor them with all the functions of life, and we can react immediately to crisis in the patient in this car, on the scene of the road accident, and we can react in the fastest way you can imagine.' They're so well organized that they use a computer to decide whether it's quicker to send a helicopter or the MICU to the crash.

Speed is important, says Dr Schmidt: 'Seconds count in helping the patients. It's so important to have free airways, to get enough oxygen to the brain, because otherwise it will sustain serious or irreparable damage.'

A large number of specialists is needed on the scene of any serious crash: fire-fighters, ambulance crew, the traffic police, specialist photographers. As PC Mike Doyle, of the Accident Investigation Unit of the West Midlands Police, points out, 'Maybe even scenes-of-crime officers are necessary for certain types of accident, other officers to perhaps close off roads and help with traffic direction and then at some stage an accident investigator will be requested.

'The accident investigator will make a tour of the accident site, examine both the condition of the road and any marks that are on the road left by vehicles, bodies, any debris positions, and they're all marked, generally with wax chalk or spray paint so that if any conditions change such as weather conditions we've got those items marked in position and we can measure them with either electronic measurement equipment or by use of physical tapes. Essentially it's a data-collection process first off, and then that information is brought into this office and we will produce from electronic measurements, from surveys, a plan of the scene which will include everything that's necessary, skid marks, body positions, pools of blood, they are necessary sometimes because it may show the final position where a body lay. It's not a very pleasant thing to relate to people but it's sometimes the only way that we can define where a person finally ended up.

'Once we've downloaded the information on to the computer and produced a plan, that's when the maths work begins, because generally at least two or three skid tests will have been done at the scene from a set speed in a vehicle with similar braking characteristics, but more importantly if at all possible the same vehicle is used. If we use the same vehicle, if it's got any braking defects or any other unusual characteristics, we're going to get the same braking values at certain speeds, that is if at 40 m.p.h. it skidded 20 metres, then if we drive it at 40 m.p.h. and get a 20-metre skid mark to match in with the accident displacement, we can say yes, that car was travelling at 40 m.p.h. when the accident happened. We will then take the information from skid tests and, by matching it against the skid marks from the accident vehicle, calculate an initial speed for the vehicle. That's the most basic discipline, speed from skid marks, where a vehicle skids to a stop.

'Another basic discipline is "pedestrian throw" because we're calculating the point of impact to the final position of a body. If you imagine just how violently a person is lifted by a vehicle on impact, certain movements of the feet across the road surface will leave a scuff-mark trace, so whenever an investigator attends the scene of an accident where a pedestrian's been struck, the first thing that he or she will look at are the shoes of the pedestrian, to see if there are any scuff marks shown on the soles and what colour the shoes are because that can be matched in with any mark that might be on the road surface. If that scuff mark is found, a speed can be calculated for the pedestrian at impact.'

Doyle recounted one recent case where tyre evidence had proved crucial: a large lorry drove straight instead of turning into a sweeping left-hand bend on an urban motorway. It hit three cars, and the driver of one was killed. The lorry driver and the owner of the vehicle claimed that there had been a burst tyre before impact 'but we have video footage of that particular collision and when we looked at the video footage there was no kind of deviation from the straight line. The driver wasn't fighting to maintain control of the vehicle, it just went straight across the carriageway into the path of the saloon vehicle. Now, vehicle tyres are designed to be able to be deflated and still allow you to stop pretty well in a straight line, but you would need to steer to maintain that straight line position because if you didn't realize that the tyre had deflated and you were able to just carry on driving normally and to encounter perhaps a bend, then that wouldn't be very safe at all. So you have to have some indication that it's deflated, whether it be a slight pull to one side or noise of the rim running on the road. Certainly in this instance we were able to prove by looking at the tape, examining the scene: if a tyre had deflated we would have expected what we would term deflation or scallop marks on the road surface from the tyre before impact and there weren't any of those in evidence and so that mitigation was overruled.'

So tyres, and the marks they make, are routinely tested for 'grinding patches' to see if there has been a skid. As we have seen, skid marks are vital and revealing evidence – though they're not made, as one might imagine, by rubber burning onto the road, but by the heat of the tyre rubbing on it and bringing the lighter elements and impurities in the bitumen to the surface. There are two types of skid mark: the 'shadows', which last only a short time, and more permanent marks, which can help trace the movement of a vehicle after a crash. The detectives can test the tarmac at the site of the accident to see if it is too smooth to provide proper adhesion. A car is driven along the road and put into a skid; as the brakes are applied a pneumatic gun fires a pellet of chalk down onto the road. The distance is measured between the start of braking and the point at which the car stops. If there are no skid marks, they resort to a technique known as 'momentum exchange', momentum being the weight of a body multiplied by the speed at which it is travelling.

Technical expressions like 'momentum exchange' conceal grim realities. Inevitably, as with anyone arriving at a scene of horror and chaos, the 'detectives' must not allow themselves to become emotionally involved. 'Impartiality is the word within accident investigation,' says PC Mike Doyle, 'remaining impartial when we're dealing with the accident, right the way through to the court – or even preventing a court case. Sometimes accident investigation may not be "Let's get someone to court and deal with them", it may be, "Well, witnesses have said things about this person and he or she wasn't speeding," or "That's completely wrong because the laws of physics wouldn't allow it" and we will try to prove or disprove that.'

But even he has to admit that 'When you go out to these accidents you can't become personally involved immediately. Maybe you can show a bit of emotion later, and that's a terrible thing to say but you have to be professional. If we weren't impartial and completely professional, we'd miss things or we might draw conclusions before we know what's actually happened at the accident. We're there to make sure that every accident is investigated thoroughly, and that we get the correct result at the end in technical terms, not emotional terms.'

To help the detectives cope with the inevitable traumas from dealing day in and day out with horrors, Malcolm Westwood's team has 'a critical incident debriefing whereby when it's perceived that a traumatic incident has affected fire-fighters – when they've gone home and they're thinking about it and churn it over in the middle of the night – we invoke this procedure where somebody comes down and talks to them. It would be wrong to call it counselling but it's certainly a method by which people can examine what they saw, how they feel and, of course, find out that their colleagues feel exactly the same thing.'

To cope with the stress, says Doyle, 'We laugh and joke with each other, not about accidents but about silly things that happen in the office, things that happen when we're out and about, and just try to maintain a balance because the emotion's there. But occasionally it all gets too much.' Dr Anthony Bleetman agrees. He is fully aware that 'It is not our job to be judgemental and we should never become judgemental. However, if I'm being honest with you, I would have to say that I cannot help but get annoyed or very upset when I see victims from road accidents that have been caused perhaps by drunk drivers or by joy-riders. I think that is a tragedy and at times I have found it extremely difficult not to air my views.' However, he claims that he has only snapped once, when he dragged the drunken driver of a stolen car into the room where he 'had just been up to the elbows inside the chest of the drunk's fifteen-year-old girl-friend', who died. At least Bleetman forced the youth to witness the results of his actions.

Birmingham, the epicentre of Britain's motorway network, has long been a pioneer in the scientific and medical treatment of crashes. The regional training centre where Mike Doyle works is one of only five in Britain devoted to accident investigation, where a team of three train up to a dozen officers at a time. According to Doyle, 'We train them in basic technical aspects to do with accident investigation. We teach them various disciplines, such as calculating speed from skid marks, calculating critical speed, which is where a vehicle's travelling around a bend or corner at the limit of its adhesion to the road surface – it's actually slipping sideways. We teach them how to calculate the speed of a vehicle when it's impacted with a pedestrian.'

Back at the police station, all this information can be plotted and the speed estimated, not only because excessive speed is still the most frequent cause of a crash but because the speed of impact will determine the likelihood of internal injuries to the victims. Each member of a team will have his own role, although, says Doyle, 'All the members of a team will be able to deal with every aspect of an accident, each will specialize – in pedestrians, the identification of debris at the scene, how to match debris to a particular vehicle, critical speed, or momentum exchange.'

The most obvious source of evidence is, of course, the eye-witness but, as Doyle says, there are times when 'they will have to rationalize what's happened in an accident because it may be the first time they've ever seen an accident. They will try to make sense of what they've heard and then seen – or not; because sometimes the sound of impact will make a person turn round and they will explain the accident from the vehicle approaching at speed and striking someone. We won't be able to confirm that they turned round at a certain time but we may be able to confirm that the vehicle wasn't travelling at speed. Although we're not saying that they're telling lies, they may have mentally conjured up the image to cope with the situation and that's all it is. People can fall into that trap. Remember that they're not professional witnesses. They're just any person who might be out on the street or in a car and happen, unfortunately, to see or be involved in this serious accident and they will want answers and they will want answers that fit in with their rationale.'

Nevertheless, eye-witnesses were once relied on to provide estimates of the speed at which a vehicle was travelling. As Murray Mackay puts it: 'Once you started to calculate speed from skid marks you're using the standard Newtonian equations, which were not recognized in British courts at the time. So I spent a happy two years travelling around the courts saying that last Tuesday at eight p.m. in Burton-on-Trent high street the laws of Newtonian motion were in force, as well as everywhere else in the universe as far as I know.' This explanation would be followed by detailed questioning as to the nature of these laws and how they affected his estimate of the speed at which the vehicle was travelling.

Those involved in a crash are not necessarily the best witnesses: they're confused and they conceal things – for instance, not telling the truth as to whether they were wearing seat-belts. They may not even be able to remember the crash. 'The reason for that,' says Dr Bob Gunther, 'is not because they've buried the memory, it's because they never had it. If there's a serious trauma that causes a decrease in their awareness or an injury to the head, the result is that the memory never consolidates. They have nothing to remember. It's not really a protective mechanism as much as a biological fact. When the same thing happens in a computer, if you're working on a document and you unplug it before storing it on the hard drive, it's gone. It's the same kind of process.

'Many people do remember the crash and the moment of impact vividly. During the crash, there's the experience of dissociation. We all have an awareness, just under the surface, of possibly being involved in a serious motor-vehicle accident, a crash, but we keep it under the surface. Suddenly one day we lose control, the car isn't responding, it's sliding, skidding, we're approaching another vehicle, approaching a tree, a bridge abutment, and that awareness that we've kept buried floods our mind, we dissociate, time stretches, our attention is somewhat diffuse. It's as if we're looking through a film, through a screen. Detail can be either enhanced or lost depending on the person's state of mind but perception definitely changes and the moment of impact can seem to take minutes rather than being the split second that it really is.'

To make matters more confusing, he says, 'After the accident those people who can remember it typically replay it over and over again endlessly. If they have flashbacks it can be as if the accident is happening right now. Even if that isn't happening they remember the accident again and again and again. They may have nightmares, dreaming of it happening over and over again, and as that happens they become more and more anxious. Now, the awareness of the danger of being in a motor vehicle can't be repressed, and many people lose the confidence even to ride in a car, become essentially phobic,' a state of mind that does not encourage accurate recall of their trauma. They may also be suffering from that now well-known phenomenon, survivor guilt, first identified among those who had emerged alive from the Nazi concentration camps. 'For many people who survive crashes where somebody else has lost their life, it's not uncommon for there to be some kind of survivor guilt,' says Dr Gunther. 'The person feels as if it should have been them, especially if it's someone close to them, a friend, family member, a child. Not uncommonly they'll be overwhelmed with this sense of responsibility, even though they're sitting in the back seat and couldn't possibly have caused or prevented the accident.'

Eye-witness perceptions are never more inaccurate than when dealing with motorcycles. As Mike Doyle points out, 'Motorcycles are generally quite noisy and a motorcycle passing across someone's vision can appear to be absolutely hurtling along if they don't get a full view of it in approach and exit, if it's just a sort of flash between buildings or between parked vehicles. Because it's noisy and because it was there and gone in a flash they may turn round and say, "Well, he was doing 70, 80 m.p.h. along the road," and we may be able to prove that the speed was far less.'

The biggest trauma for the detectives, however, comes not at the scene of the crash, but afterwards, when they have to visit the relatives of those involved. 'Whenever a fatality occurs within a family group,' says Doyle, 'the first thing is that the person that was there obviously isn't there anymore. It's a major loss to any family. What people want to know is where the victim was going and how the crash happened, and not just that they were driving along and another car pulled across in front of them and killed them. They want to know speeds, and they want to know – more importantly, I suppose – whether or not there was any suffering. We can't really say with certainty whether or not a person underwent any sort of pain during an accident. Sometimes when we've investigated the accident thoroughly we will, if requested, sit down with the victim's family and go through the complete reconstruction and normally that's something that's done in coroner's court.

'We have a very good coroner in Birmingham who can flow through any incident and let people know exactly what happened without making it too upsetting. It's always going to be upsetting but he tries very hard to maintain a lot of compassion during the hearings and we try to continue that afterwards with a certain amount of victim support. We will visit relatives and show them, almost guide them, through the reconstruction from beginning to end and any questions at all that they need to ask us we will try to answer them.'

The American equivalent of Birmingham, the city where the science of crash detection is most advanced, is perhaps Dade County, around Miami. There, the US government is funding several studies; one concentrates not on what happened to the car but to the person inside it. To Americans any death in a traffic accident is defined as homicide. Hence Robert Jones, a veteran with Metro Dade County Police, calls himself a 'traffic homicide investigator'. As he says, 'We conduct the same investigations, the same scrutiny. The uniformed units that get there first have an obligation to preserve the crime scene, the road evidence, to prevent it from being moved or marked up or destroyed. We're notified, we respond, we do field sketch drawings, we process vehicles, we interview the drivers and witnesses, we photograph the scene, and then we are able to determine through the investigation if it was an alcohol-related incident or due to reckless criminal activity. Our main function, being a police agency, is criminal investigation. We go there not as civil investigators but as criminal investigators.'

Cases vary, of course. Jones gave two different scenarios: 'One would be if someone was driving in a reckless and wilfully wanton manner where they're late for an appointment and they're speeding and there's witnesses to that. We can prove probable cause on that if they have a crash and end up killing or seriously injuring someone. Then they would be arrested on those charges. Another scenario [would be] if we had an individual driving his car and he's going down the road and he tries to beat the light. The chances are that he'll still be charged but he won't be charged with a felony, a criminal law offence. He'd be an infractional type of case where the chances are if he's convicted in the state of Florida on fatality cases, he would lose his driver's licence for a minimum of one year and be fined and he would have to do community service, things like that.' But, Jones emphasizes, '90 per cent of the time we'll know immediately if it's going to be a criminal case'.

Whatever their differences in approach, the procedures adopted by the crash detectives on both sides of the Atlantic are much the same. Once Jones and his colleagues have talked to the policemen at the scene, got the feel of what happened and received the witness statements, 'I look at the scene and make sure that the statements and the scene are pretty much accurate, then I photograph my scene. Once I conduct my photographs I diagram the scene. Then I go over the statements with the people who have written them to be sure that they're similar to what they verbally told me. I put them aside for the case file. I then take aerial photographs if it's during the daytime. That assists us in our diagramming and placement of evidence. After that's done we conduct vehicle processing, where we look at the vehicles and determine what could have caused the crash from the vehicle standpoint – if there was defective equipment maybe. When we are diagramming and photographing we are also looking at the scene and determining what type of scene evidence, roadway evidence, came into play. Once we take care of the vehicle processing and the witness statements, then we will go to the hospitals where the injured will be and attempt to get statements from those parties. Often we can't get statements from critically injured people for a while. Sometimes we never get a statement from them because they refuse to talk to us. Then if a victim is deceased, we get the autopsy report from their injuries.'

Evidence is much the same the world over. According to Jones, 'The first thing we're looking for when we arrive on the scene is pre-collision skids, seeing if the party saw the danger prior to the crash and if they did, did they have time to react. It helps us in the reconstruction and the calculations of speeds. We look and determine and locate area of collisions. We don't have accidents in this state, they're crashes. That'll give us our approach angles, where the vehicle was approaching from, then we look for the area of collision for departure angles, where the vehicles depart from. Where they go into, where they collide and go on to maximum engagement and then they separate and go on to their departure angles – that all comes in as part of the field sketch. The reason those are important is that they give us our speed calculations where we can get exact speeds at impact. We can then calculate the speed of each vehicle at impact and if they've done pre-collision braking we can add that on and get an exact speed prior to them seeing the danger, so we can find out the speed they were travelling prior to braking. 'It's a tragic, but sadly necessary routine.

By the time the detectives have got their victims to hospital their work is complete and they can leave their charges with another new breed, the doctors who specialize in road accidents.

The Medics: Survival is Not Enough

Almost every conceivable violent confrontation between the
automobile and its occupants was listed: mechanisms of passenger
ejection, the geometry of knee-cap and hip-joint injuries, deformation
of passenger compartments in head-on and rear-end collisions,
injuries sustained in accidents at roundabouts, at trunk-road
intersections, at the junctions between access roads and motorway
intersections, the telescoping mechanisms of car-bodies in front-end
collisions, abrasive injuries formed in roll-overs, the amputation of
limbs by roof assemblies and door sills during roll-over, facial injuries
caused by rear-view mirrors and sun-visors, whiplash injuries in rear-
end collisions, first- and second-degree burns in accidents involving
the rupture and detonation of fuel tanks, chest injuries caused by
steering column impalements, abdominal injuries caused by faulty
seat-belt adjustment, second-order collisions between front-seat and
rear-seat passengers, cranial and spinal injuries caused by ejection
through windshields, the graded injuries to the skull caused by
variable wind-shield glasses, injuries to minors, both children and
infants in arms, injuries caused by prosthetic limbs, injuries caused
within cars fitted with invalid controls, the complex self-amplifying
injuries of single and double amputees, injuries caused by specialist
automobile accessories such as record players, cocktail cabinets and
radio-telephones, the injuries caused by manufacturers' medallions,
safety belt pinions and quarter-window latches.

J. G. Ballard, *Crash*

It is sad but true that many advances in medicine, above all in surgery, are
the direct result of wars and other man-induced horrors. Obvious examples
include plastic surgery in the Second World War and the treatment of bomb
wounds suffered by the victims of terrorist outrages as a result of the
Troubles in Northern Ireland. To these can now be added the treatment of
trauma as a result of increased attention to the victims of road accidents.
From the number of victims of particular injuries seen by doctors, especially
those who specialize in road accidents, several new ideas have emerged, and
far more specific treatments. One of the most curious aspects of this – above
all for the doctors – is that their patients are usually young, have been
relatively healthy and have had to be treated for injuries that had either been
relatively rare before the widespread use of the car or, as with fractures,
usually associated with the old and sick. This inevitably changed priorities
and attitudes.

Dr Burgess, at the Cowley Shock Trauma Hospital in Baltimore, is the
opposite number of Dr Howard Baderman in Birmingham. 'At first it was

what I would call anecdotal science and the standard joke among us is the "journal of anecdotal medicine". We were successful in getting grants to step into some science and to send an accident investigation team so that we had more than just the ambulance driver's report. We took the car apart and re-created on a computer programme the exact circumstances of the accident, much akin to what the Birmingham Accident Centre has been doing for years. We had the full accident investigation team come to the table, we had the emergency medical personnel who saw the circumstances when the patient was pulled out. Finally we added a basic science group, with our colleagues at the University of Virginia, who were then going to try to re-create the circumstance with dummies or computer modelling, or in some cases cadavers, and see if we were right, the next step being the design of vehicles that would mitigate that injury pattern.'

The work of doctors and medical researchers like Dr Burgess starts not with the second collision, between the body of the victim and the interior of the vehicle, but with the third collision. This, as he points out, 'is where the injuries are truly caused, in the collision between the internal organs and the body wall. It might be the heart and the aorta that collide with the inside wall of the chest. In the brain cavity, in the skull, the brain collides with the frontal wall of the skull and that's where the injury often truly occurs. That's all in the third collision.' Fortunately, the introduction of restraint systems has helped.

As Professor Mackay points out, 'Specific injuries can be related to particular components in the vehicle. The simplest case is thoracic damage caused by the steering assembly when, for example, the curvature of the wheel rim can be matched to exterior bruising on the chest. Door-handles, knobs and switches on the instrument panel, and fittings such as interior lights on the door pillar or roof, all give rise to specific injury, and allow the seating positions of the occupants to be established.'

Naturally the first medical priority has always been to ensure that the victim lived, although after that specialists concentrated on specific injuries. As Dr Burgess says: 'The original databases, the political pressure and everything was for survival and appropriately so. All of industry's engineering and all of government's political power went towards getting a living patient or driver out of that vehicle once the crash had occurred. Not as much engineering was put into the lower-extremity injuries, for instance, and appropriately so because they didn't threaten life, but as we watched the data, people were surviving now much higher-energy crashes with very little thought given to their lower extremities. Those injuries had always been there in the population pool but they'd usually been attached to an unfortunate individual who didn't survive. Now we had very healthy people in every other way with pretty significant injuries to their lower extremities and they came in predictable patterns.

'In this case there was additional interest because of the economic cost and the fact that traditional databases didn't pick this up because it wasn't a threat to life, but as we started plotting the injury, the long rehabilitation times, the cost to society and the insurance company, and the time lost from work et cetera, it became a significant research topic. The patterns are predictable, and many patients looked like somebody would look if they tried to commit suicide or jumped from a burning house, landing on their ankle with a high degree of axial load, all the pressure coming up from the heel. Certainly, somebody conscious of an accident about to happen extends themselves and is bracing for the accident and the force delivered through the floorboard, either directly or via the pedals if one foot is planted on the brake pedal, is very much akin to what a person encounters when they fall from a height and land on their feet.

'That helped us, first, assign a risk factor to this, and second to try to work with the industry on how we're going to mitigate it. We don't just want you to survive the accident any more, we want you to survive, get out of the car, walk to your family, be able to take a hike with your children and earn a living on your feet, so that's part of the pattern recognition too.'

The worst type of damage that can be sustained is to the brain, which requires a special type of investigation, and an investigator like Faris Bandak, a researcher into biomechanics for the US Department of Transport. As he points out, 'In the United States alone each year nearly fifty thousand people die of this injury and a million almost are treated for traumatic brain injury. This not only affects individuals indiscriminately, young and old, it also disrupts the community and when it gets to society it becomes a major economic problem because you have people who are dysfunctional and people who require lots of care and attention and are unable to be productive and take care of themselves. Motor-vehicle crashes are responsible for nearly half of all traumatic brain injury in the United States. Historically, brain injuries were the leading cause of death and disability. As we have come to the age of sophisticated restraint systems, like air-bags, there is a decline in brain injuries, but they're still the leading cause of high-severity injuries.'

The problem starts when the car stops: 'It tries to transmit the message to you that it's stopping mechanically but you keep moving. The first impact on your head occurs to the skull from some component of the car, the windshield, the steering wheel or the headers. Then the brain follows that same path by also continuing to move. Since the skull has now stopped, the brain is continuing to move and injury begins at that stage.

'There are two types of injury: impact injury and non-impact injury. Impact injury is when you have direct contact with some object, and non-impact injuries are associated with acceleration where the brain really just rocks without hitting something. The latter is the type of injury that a boxer would experience when he gets hit, particularly on the chin, which results in brain movement that causes distortion to the neural structure. That distortion is what knocks out the boxer. When the brain rotates it deforms inside the skull, then it stretches components of the brain called axons. When those are stretched you end up with an injury. The same event occurs in a car crash, maybe when your head hits something and it's rotated back or forth, or even when it doesn't hit something, when you're stopped with a seat-belt and your head rotates. There can be significant rotations in the brain that are similar to the sort of rotations that a boxer would sustain and the same neural damage would occur. This damage could be as severe as coma, or a mild injury, which is basically a concussion that reverses because these axons stretch and they come back.

'We try to understand the mechanisms of brain injury so that we can provide technology and science to help build safety restraints, seat-belts and air-bags. We look at what it takes to injure a brain in real situations, we look at the impact of a crash and what level of loading it takes to injure the brain and then we recommend that that level not be exceeded in a car crash.'

The first obvious problem that distinguishes the study of injuries to the brain from those to other parts of the body is that 'our models are only as good as the information we put in them. For example, for a broken leg you can test that breaking strength with cadavers. With the brain you can't do that, you have to have a living brain.' Bandak and his colleagues use the findings of the specialists who reconstruct exactly what happened in a specific crash. This provides them with 'the evidence from that situation, for example where the head hit, all the markers, how much crush and what the velocities are, and you can model that using dummies and computer models. The brain is unique in its demands for information and a dead brain does not give you the information that's necessary. We are unable to see physically what happens inside the brain so we try to simulate that with devices that have the same consistency and the same type of structure as the brain and particularly with computer modelling, which we use to try to simulate what happens in a car crash, and get more detail of the interactions of the brain, the dynamics of the brain with the inside of the skull. From the data that safety reconstruction specialists give us, we can tune our models so that they become realistic in car crashes. Then we can take what is basically a full human model with a human head on it in a car and repeat crashes, and try to look at the response of the brain for each crash scenario.'

The modelling involves the very latest in computer-created virtual reality to re-create that inordinately complex mechanism, the human brain. The CAT and MRI* scans, says Bandak, are 'rich with information, geometric information and material information that we need to make up these

*Computer Assisted Tomograph and Magnetic Resonance Imaging

Ralph Nader, campaigner extraordinaire, in characteristically insistent mode in 1970.
(*POPPERFOTO*)

The Volkswagen Beetle, almost as dangerous a vehicle as the Chevrolet Corvair.
(*ALDO TORELLI/TONY STONE IMAGES*)

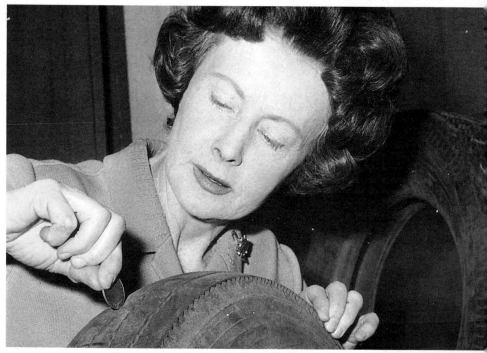

The grim reality of salvage work – the white stuff is not snow but the foam from a modern fire-hose.
(PA NEWS/DAVID JONES)

Below Left: The charismatic Barbara Castle, showing just how little tread there was on a worn tyre.
(PA NEWS)

Below: The expert face of modern rescue.
(BRUCE AYRES/TONY STONE IMAGES)

Left: Today, crash-test dummies are made in every shape and size ...
(*Michael Rosenfeld/Tony Stone Images*)

Right: ... including the most pregnant of passengers.
(*Andy Sacks/Tony Stone Images*)

Below: Dummies were in use in the United States – albeit only for publicity purposes – as early as 1962.
(*Popperfoto*)

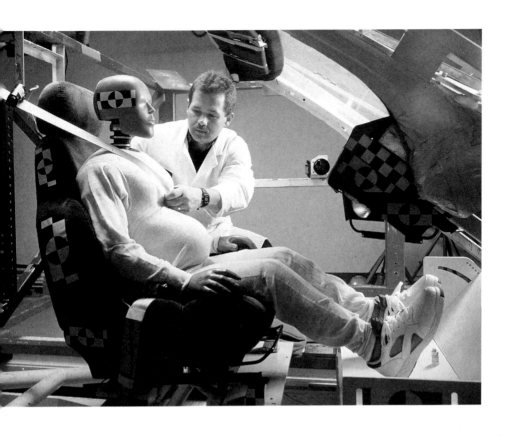

Above: Resignation in the face of disaster, on the M42 near Birmingham, following two multiple pile-ups in the fog.
(POPPERFOTO)

Views of typical large-scale motorway disasters, in the United States (above, right) and in Britain (right and overleaf).
(ABOVE, RIGHT: ANDY SACKS/TONY STONE IMAGES;
RIGHT: DAVE HARTLEY/REX FEATURES;
OVERLEAF: LIONEL GUNS/REX FEATURES)

models. From those CAT scans, we construct a three-dimensional model which is a true physical model that behaves like a true head with a true brain inside it. Of course we all vary, one head varies quite a bit from another, and through our studies we are trying to find the generic head so to speak, the head that has the features that most of us have so that that can be used as injury rather than a specific head for a specific person.

'Once you model that situation again, reconstructing it, you get the loads on the head and you try to validate those loads by what you saw in the field. When you're comfortable enough that they're realistic loads, then you can apply them to the computer models and try to see in detail in that particular crash what happened to the brain. How did the brain move inside the skull? What's the likelihood of this type of injury versus that type? That information feeds back to us – the safety community that is interested in prevention – so that this doesn't happen again. It also feeds to the treatment side, the physicians, who then can understand from the causes what they can't see.

'In many of the closed head injuries that come in, there are no visible signs. You have to look inside with the various imaging scans and try to discern what happened. But the bleeding after the fact could be from anywhere so knowing the mechanical markers, and tuning your thinking to those mechanical markers, you can with the help of computers try to focus on that type of injury and try to get into the particular intervention that's necessary.'

The continuing detective work carried on in hospitals on a number of other parts of the body can affect both medicine and the safety of vehicles. The first body part in which Dr Burgess could recognize a pattern of injuries was the pelvis. Why? He says, 'It's such a large singular structure right in the middle of our body. It's a circle and it protects a lot of local organs. Because of its circular geometry, as it's injured it tells a story – the direction from which the force has come and the amount of violence that's been generated to the body. For a few years we found that very interesting on a local level to help us treat the pelvic injury and then we found a secondary benefit quickly thereafter: predictable patterns of associated injury could be found. If the diameter of the pelvis was acutely shortened, as in one hit from the side, it told a story about risk factors to internal injuries that had also taken a hit from the side. This included things like the spleen and the liver, depending on the side, contusion to the lung, diaphragm rupture, actual measurable amount of thoracic aorta injury. Specific patterns of neck and head injury could be predicted from the pelvis, not 100 per cent, of course, but general patterns of injury. In the same way, going forward – a typical case of that would be over the handlebars of your motorcycle – would open your pelvis wide, expose you to a lot of tears in blood vessels and put your life at risk from local bleeding. The pelvis was the prototype.'

This did not imply that all the injuries were the same, for, as Dr Burgess explains, the pattern was complicated: 'It's almost infinitely dependent on the position of the leg during the impact. People of different stature drive with their legs in different positions, people of different genders drive with their legs in different positions, and so because the position may be widely abducted or very demure, with the knees almost together, it delivers the blow, if it comes via the thigh-bone, in two different directions and gives you two separate injury patterns. The standard remark among many of us is that there's about fourteen positions you can sit in that we catalogue.' But there are exceptions beyond the 'standard' fourteen. Frighteningly, 'People drive with one foot out the window, using cruise control, in North America frequently. The predominance of the automatic transmission allows the left leg to be in many positions and whether the patient sees the accident about to happen or not adds to whether they'll extend their leg in the act of braking just before impact. The patterns are almost infinite.'

Sad, but typical of medical progress in times of violence, was the way in which progress was accelerated by the huge number of crashes and victims. Examining the wounds 'in the accident ward or emergency room, one would get the sense of what had occurred at the moment of impact. After watching a few hundred of these patients and collecting the data in detail we saw a predictable pattern of injury to the organs just above, and I think it made us better physicians and nurses.

'We found that our ability to predict the injuries from a first examination and X-ray was valuable in saving lives. We found that that allowed us to resuscitate those patients better. One of the benefits of knowing what had happened was that we could actually close this pelvis in our accident ward with some hardware we have now available as soon as they come off the helicopter – inside the human body this is the internal version of applying pressure to a bleeding external wound. It makes the space into which bleeding occurs much smaller and it slows down the bleeding. It's like pressing your thumb on a bleeding artery externally.'

Even today pattern recognition remains the key to progress. Dr Burgess says: 'Pattern recognition has brought itself from the clinician, through the accident reconstruction, back to the basic scientists and hopefully the loop there continues to the automobile manufacturer who takes the data and changes the vehicle.'

Since 1971 Saab has been investigating road accidents in Sweden that involve one of its cars. The exercise is designed not only to provide statistical information but also to enable Saab's doctor to look at the medical aspects of the crash. This has led to such developments as an 'active' head restraint, designed to reduce the often-severe impact on the neck as a result of rear-end collisions: 'whiplash' is caused when the head moves violently in relation to the body so Saab has reduced the impact by connecting the back and head rests.

In the past, as we have seen, the doctors' primary concern was simply with the survival of victims, but today considerable effort is being made to ensure that they resume an active life – and, crucially from an economic point of view, not remain a charge on the community or, in the United States, on an insurance company.

American motorists usually carry comprehensive insurance when driving, which can give rise to enormous claims. Kenny O'Brien reckons that the disabling injuries he sustained from a crash has cost his insurance company well over a million dollars – and that's only in the first two years after the crash. Nevertheless, as he says: 'We pay very little. Our health insurance picked up a lot of the medical bills and some things for later care, but everything that they don't pay our car insurance does because the accident happened in the car.' And if the accident had not been in a car? Kenny O'Brien can't even imagine the horrifying consequences: 'A couple of people I met while I was in the hospital had their accident either swimming or on a trampoline and they had their medical bills paid for by their health insurance but whatever they don't cover they have to pay out of their pocket or keep fighting health insurance for, so I don't know how I would ever get by that way. I'm just very glad that we deal with the car insurance.'

But the pressure to get victims back to an ordinary working life creates complicated problems. Dr Burgess gives the example of a severe ankle injury, which is 'no threat to life but our "outcomes" research has shown that by six months, although it's healed this patient never walks without pain. Many such victims can't earn a living, they can't stand at a drill press or a desk or a kitchen or they can't take care of their children. They can't go back to recreation.

'So besides protecting from the big dramatic injuries, a lot of our research and engineering efforts have gone into redesigning the toe pin and pedal area to mitigate these injuries, not as dramatic, not as life-threatening but every bit as costly, especially because these patients are now consuming resources from out-of-work insurance. We hope the early part of the next decade will deliver a combination of living patients who get up intact and leave their vehicle, the whole of the accident being somehow controlled, the whole of the energy force, to save their life from the neck down to the pelvis and save their long-term function.'

Dr Burgess is well placed to judge the overall contribution of motor-connected medical research because he works at the Cowley Centre at the University of Maryland. This is named after the man who recognized two crucial factors in the new discipline: the Golden Hour, the period immediately after the crash in which so many lives can be saved, and the concept of trauma as a specific disease. It had taken doctors some time to grasp that trauma was a specific problem, unrelated to the part of the body where the injuries were located. 'Because,' says Dr Burgess, 'our profession had broken us up into neuro-surgeons and chest surgeons and orthopaedic surgeons and facial surgeons and vascular surgeons, we forced that patient into that model, and the neuro-surgeon was called for the head injury and the bone-injury doctor was called to take care of the bones. They might arrive or dispense at different times, there was frequently a turf battle for which injury was the most important with everybody else as sort of an adjunct consultant.

'To his credit Cowley and some of the European trauma centres, most notably the Germans in Hanover, started to address that traumatized patient with the trauma being considered a disease entity. It makes sense – you can't break both femurs or thigh-bones without the products of that almost explosive fracture pattern getting into your bloodstream. The moment you break both femurs in an accident, bone fragments, fat and marrow products are circulating in your blood or they're up in your lungs, they go to your brain, they go to your kidneys, your liver, everywhere, your bloodstream is full of them. You can't ask your brain to oxygenate well and deliver good oxygen once your lungs are compromised, either by a direct blow or by aspiration of your stomach contents when you get hit.'

Thanks to pattern recognition, the pioneers of trauma medicine were able to bring together and reconcile the differing views. The important thing, says Dr Burgess, was that it got 'that multi-disciplinary team in the same room. What had happened in the past I think is the epidemiologists collected data three months after accidents occurred – where they occurred, sex, age, and whatever. The clinicians were interested in the mechanics of fixing the injury, the accident reconstructionists had a car, they reconstructed it but they didn't know what happened to the occupants, and our basic science colleagues in labs who worked with dummies and cadavers and computer modelling didn't have anyone sitting in the corner saying, "That's interesting data but we don't see that injury pattern anywhere in the real world. Could you please try to reconstruct your experimental format so that it gives relevant data?" I think the most gratifying thing that began with pattern recognition was that we made a good enough case with it to get federal funding to put us all in the same room, with one surgeon in charge, and that's where I think the advances have truly come from – the best sciences from the pure science lab, the best clinical experiences from trauma centres like this.

'As the world-wide scientific community started to recognize that all these systems were interrelated, issues of timing, of fixing certain injuries and their relative benefit and risk to the other systems, are now the hot topics in trauma medicine.' Not surprisingly perhaps, the doctors found that repairing fractures, for instance, greatly helped the survival rate and reduced the incidence of infection. Equally, Dr Burgess says, 'Aggressive and early treatment of the lungs has some obvious benefits, so treating as a disease entity was therefore helpful.'

Once trauma was recognized as a disease in its own right, says Burgess, and 'when you start plotting the reasons for it, you can apply some public-health type agendas where you can study it with epidemiologists or whatever and see why it is occurring. Is it roadway design in the crashes? You start sampling all your drivers. Are many of them compromised with drugs or alcohol? Is that an avenue to apply disease education, public-health measures? If you see certain patterns that drive patterns of violence and trauma into a centre, you ask, Is it poverty, lack of jobs, the type of family structure?

'Trauma primarily occurs to young people, often high risk-takers, and it takes them out in their first productive years, so there is every reason we should put a lot of resources into it. But trauma has been a disease for the young physician. Before it got its marker as a specific disease it was assigned to the most junior house officer – it's just a fracture, it's just an accident ward. The experienced consultants, physicians and surgeons were in bed at night waiting for the disease entity the next day on their schedule.'

The most significant result of the recognition of trauma as a specific disease has been the adoption of an American system of trauma management called Advanced Trauma Life Support. ATLS, which is recognized the world over as a revolutionary advance in accident medicine, systematizes the way doctors approach a traumatized patient. The object, says Dr Anthony Bleetman, 'is to ensure that there is minimal chance of overlooking serious life-threatening injuries. Once they are found, they are dealt with immediately, which is perhaps different from the way in which the rest of medicine is practised. In medicine you take a history, you examine the patient, you think a little bit, do some diagnostic tests, reach a working diagnosis and then plan treatment. In the management of trauma the situation is reversed: we're treating the life-threatening injuries as we find them while we're examining the patient.'

Unfortunately, but typically, there are still only a few units which specialize in a type of medicine that affects far more lives than many better-publicized and better-funded specialities.

One of the few such centres in the United States is the Rider Trauma Centre, at the Jackson Memorial Hospital in Miami, Florida, where Jeffrey Augenstein, a Professor of Surgery at the University of Miami School of Medicine, is a trauma surgeon. The Rider Trauma Centre opened in 1992 and, says Augenstein, 'It's one of the only facilities in this country that is designed and built to deal largely with the disease we call trauma. We deal with everything from the initial resuscitation and evaluation of patients through their rehabilitation.' His building is specially designed to ease the flow, as it were, with a heliport on the roof for the two in five patients who are airlifted to the hospital with a speedy lift to the resuscitation area.

To Dr Augenstein, trauma is unquestionably 'a disease . . . Our change in attitude came about because a study called Injury In America was published to point out that this really is a disease. It follows the same public-health types of principles as other diseases and as a result we need to address everything from prevention through the rehabilitation of people involved in the disease. I think we get into trouble when we use the word accident and imply that there is no control over the possibilities of preventing or mitigating the problems of the events.'

At first Miami tried to create a network of hospitals dealing with the disease but by 1987 virtually all except the Rider Trauma Centre had dropped out of the programme. 'We moved into dealing with 100 per cent of the trauma. About 50 per cent of the trauma we deal with here is called blunt, or automobile related, and about 50 per cent is penetrating. That comes from acts of violence' – not a surprising figure, given that Miami is probably the single most violent city in the United States.

Dr Augenstein says, 'Blunt trauma or what we see in automobile-related injuries, is often difficult to diagnose and it has become even more challenging because so many more occupants are involved in crashes.' Thanks to air-bags, many occupants of severely damaged vehicles escape unharmed but there is a danger here 'of being lulled into a sense of comfort. But what we're finding in some of our data is that there's a small group of people who look pretty good at the scene but who, because of the tremendous forces imparted to them in the crash, may have sustained an abdominal injury that may not manifest itself with the decrease in blood pressure or the patient looking bad until internal bleeding has occurred to a degree that produces a problem. The trick in that group of patients is recognizing at the scene the people who look pretty good, the group that may have a problem, and then in a hospital, or particularly in a trauma environment like this, rapidly making the diagnoses so interventions can be provided.

'A lot of people who have intra-abdominal injuries today don't require surgery, but if you send somebody home and they go to karate practice that afternoon, that could be a real problem, so even though we don't operate we observe many of these patients very carefully. Take the liver: it's like a lot of the parts of the body, there's a lot of blood-flow into it and it may contain some bleeding – we've all probably had a cut in the liver that's stopped bleeding of its own accord. But if you bounce around a little bit or get kicked, that system that's maintaining the clotting may not be able to hold and you may have bleeding into the abdominal cavity or the part of your body that contains the intestines. It can leave you in a very bad state without you necessarily looking terrible until your blood pressure drops down.'

Dr Augenstein is lucky to have funding from the federal government, backed up with money from the motor manufacturers for research into crashes. 'Our understanding of how automobiles are doing comes from a number of perspectives: we have large statistical databases, we know how many people die and in what kind of car.' A national sampling study helps by giving 'some sense of what the spectrum of crashes means'.

Studies like these 'are based on dealing with the injured individual as a starting point and we ask the basic question, Why did that person get injured? We focus on modern automobile-safety technology.' This approach leads to close examination of the injuries involved. 'The detailed description of a bruise or a little laceration on the skin in the context of a lot of other things may not be terribly important, but if we're trying to position an occupant in an automobile during the crash, the position of a bruise may tell you something about where that part of the body was during the crash. In parallel, and as early as we can and very often as soon as we know about the crash, we send our crash investigators out to the scene to look at the car. We want to determine the energy that the car withstood, we want to know as much about contact points of the occupant or occupants in the car, we want to know whether safety devices like seat-belts were used properly, and that helps us put a picture together, which often says, "This contact in the car produced this injury," and, as you look at a number of those cases, patterns of injury begin to emerge.'

His research can lead to unexpected discoveries. He quotes cases where 'increased awareness of a problem helped, and I suspect there are many areas where, as we look at the real world conditions, we can translate that kind of information to car design'. The most startling results of his research concerned one of the most widely heralded safety advances of the past thirty years: the introduction of modern seat-belts. 'When automatic two-point belts came into use,' he says, 'they seemingly reduced accident injuries by up to 90 per cent, but there was something fishy about the way the federal government performed the tests. They required the test to be in a completely automated protection mode. In other words, you can't put the manual lap-belt on, you have to determine the protection to the dummy with just the automatic system in place. So if you look at the head injury numbers, if you look at the loads to the femur, they all looked very, very good with the two-point belts on. As we started looking at it, we noticed that a number of people who came into the trauma centre, who became a part of our study, had been wearing the two-point belts in the crashes that weren't even that bad, but they had pretty significant liver injuries. The way we try to understand injury is not merely to look at our one case but to go back to the statistical databases and even to the crash films and determine what's really happening.

'As we looked at the statistical databases there wasn't much mention of injuries related to the two-point belts. When our crash investigators tried to attribute a liver injury in a driver to a two-point belt, the system suggested that doesn't happen and that they should look for other causes. Many times, even though somebody may have felt the belt was the cause, it was probably attributed to something else, like the steering wheel. We then went to the crash films. There are two types available to us, one where you used dummies and one where you used cadavers, and there's more appropriate modelling of what a live human being does in a cadaver than in a dummy. We noticed something very interesting, that the so-called body geometry, the position of the body during the crash, was not what one would have expected with the lap-belt on.

'With the lap-belt on in a frontal crash you bend over at your waist and a lot of the so-called load, the forces, go into either your pelvis, which is very strong, or your shoulder, which is very strong. When you don't have the lap-belt on and you have just a two-point shoulder belt, your body geometry is such that if you're in the driver position the right upper part of your abdomen ends up taking most of that load. So instead of stopping with your strong shoulder and your pelvis, you're stopping with your liver in contact. And what was also pretty interesting to us in the so-called one o'clock direction of force, in other words the crashes where you're the driver but on the passenger corner, the injuries were very posterior in the liver, once again suggesting that you probably didn't run into the steering wheel because that would mean the injury was in the front of the liver. These injuries were all in the back of the liver, so we felt that probably the explanation for some of these liver injuries was the fact that the people were just wearing the two-point belts without the lap-belt in place. That doesn't mean that in certain crashes with the lap-belt in place you won't get a liver injury, but I think there's an extra opportunity because of your body geometry to get a liver injury, even in low-level crashes, if you only wear the two-point belt.'

This discovery had two results: first an attempt to educate drivers to use their lap-belt, and second to alert the police to cases in which the victim could have injuries not apparent at first sight. And Augenstein's research confirmed that air-bags could kill children. Now, he says, 'We're making it very clear, don't put the kid in the front of a car. I mean that's just as simple as you can get but unfortunately it took some tragedy before that occurred and it would be nice to avoid those kinds of crashes.'

6

The Cars We Deserve?

During the1960s I was writing about motoring and the motor industry and was testing regularly many of the cars on the market. But journalists and manufacturers alike were largely unaware of the work of pioneers like Murray Mackay: we were not overly concerned with the inherent safety of the vehicles we were testing, except indirectly in that we were interested in the quality of their handling and braking. In that sense, at least, we were disciples of Alec Issigonis.

Looking back on this makes me realize just how far our attitudes – as well as the cars – have changed over the past thirty years, of just how much has been done to increase the safety of the cars we drive. Many safety features that were then theoretical or experimental are now standard fittings, ranging from reversing lights (and warning hooters for lorries), lap and shoulder seat-belts front and rear, heated rear windows, with rear-window wipers and washers, internal fittings that are now sunk, padded or at least rounded, shatterproof glass, particularly on windscreens, collapsible steering wheels, and the 'three box' form of car construction by which the passenger compartment forms a relatively shock-resistant core round front and rear ends that are designed to crumple more easily.

The manufacturers are also doing their best to minimize the damage their products are doing to the world's health through the pollutants they spew into the air. Robert McNamara, however, remains severe in his judgement on the manufacturers. He points to the 'very serious problem of climate change and the auto industry. The emissions from cars are a major factor contributing to that climate problem and the auto industry has put tremendous pressure on our President to avoid the action that is required in the interest of all of us to minimize the adverse effects of climate change.' I believe he's being rather unfair: manufacturers and the major oil companies can point to an enormous reduction in the pollutants caused by their products, both in reducing car fuel consumption – largely a result of burning the fuel more efficiently – and in fuel that either contains fewer noxious substances (like lead) or releases fewer noxious gases into the atmosphere, again a result of more efficient combustion.

Behind all these developments lie major changes in attitude, in the manufacturers and in the buyers. Today some customers are positively keen on safety, and manufacturers want to sell it to them, although, as Sergeant Mike Doyle says: 'Most people pick up a car because they like the colour of it, because it's got a CD player, six-speaker sound system and velour seats and then, oh, it's got an air-bag, it's got side restraints, side-impact bars or an additional restraint system at the sides – but they seem to be low on the priorities when people look at vehicles. The higher priorities seem to be the comfort zones.' Nevertheless, over the past thirty years the situation has been transformed. General Motors now does more research into safety than any other manufacturer, while Ford has its own crash detectives. This care shows up in the figures: car ownership and mileage may be rising inexorably throughout the world, but the number of crash deaths is going down. Yet still there are appalling slips, the most obvious being the introduction by Mercedes-Benz of its 'A-class' car with its tendency to tilt or even roll over when swerving too sharply.

Nevertheless, as every motor manufacturer will tell you, however thoroughly they test their cars, in real life drivers will do things undreamed of by the engineers or their computers. Saab's studies of accidents point up their sheer randomness: 'Not one of the accidents studied on the new Saab 900,' says the company, 'has exactly the same sequence of events as any of the crash tests carried out. It would be totally inadequate to design the body structure only on the basis of collision tests in the laboratory.'

For cars to be improved, research had to show that there was a pattern in accidents, that they weren't haphazard events – an echo of the 'pattern recognition' noticed in crash injuries. Only then could the manufacturers be pressured. For Murray Mackay 'what research has shown over the years is that the best solutions have been engineering ones, rather than behavioural programmes, in terms of reducing the incidence of accidents and injuries. The engineering solutions come from better highway design, better road surfaces, better street-lights, better junction design, those sorts of things, and also from vehicle design, particularly from improving crash performance.'

In his early researches he found that 'Dominant things came out. 60 per cent of crashes are frontal. In that case if you're not wearing a seat-belt you get head injuries and face injuries from the glass, you get chest injuries from the steering wheel, you get knee injuries from the instrument panel. Those are common patterns. If you get hit from behind you get a soft-tissue neck sprain because you go backwards and your head gets extended over the seat. There are common patterns to accidents, and you can use those clearly to understand the priorities of what you should do next in terms of car. From this kind of research, you can establish the priorities in terms of regulations and in terms of car design itself, so that you can tell the designer what are the most important types of crashes, what are the most important injuries in those crashes, what are the most important parts of the car that cause those injuries and you can tell the people who write the regulations the same sorts of things so that they can focus on the major problems, the conditions, and how you regulate and design to improve those conditions.

'For instance, we've just been through an exercise in terms of side-impact design and that was based on field accident studies to establish the speeds involved, the directions of the approach of two cars, the patterns of injuries, mainly to the chest and to the abdomen and to the head in side impact, so that the regulations now reflect the reality of what comes from in-depth crash investigation.'

Behind this change – and a whole book could be written on the detailed research and consequent improvements to the safety of the cars themselves over the past thirty years – lies an equally important shift, in the buyer. As the veteran Lord Lucas puts it, thirty years ago 'safety didn't really feature. It wasn't until much later in the sixties, in the early seventies, mid-seventies, that safety became a feature. If I had to judge it against today, perhaps there was a 20 per cent safety feature in a buyer's mind in the mid-seventies. I would say that today it was probably a 70, 80 per cent feature in a buyer's mind.' Today, as he points out, 'We find that more women drive, and safety is a very much more important feature. Safety-belts, child restraints and all sort of things have now become more acceptable to the younger generation.'

Murray Mackay agrees, attributing what he terms 'a real sea change in terms of the acceptance of crash performance and safety design by the manufacturers' to 'people's awareness of it. They want to be protected and they're willing to pay for it, so it's moved from being a negative to a positive part of car design. Safety now sells cars and the companies compete against each other on just that basis. Secondly there is now a body of knowledge that's grown over the last thirty or forty years so that people can have a career in vehicle-safety engineering and safety design. There's a constituency of safety engineers within the industry who have their own arguments against styling, performance, comfort and that sort of thing, so it's here to stay.'

Of course, as cars get safer they create new problems, which can sometimes be overcome when the manufacturers accept the result of biomechanical analysis. As Jeff Crandall, of the Automobile Safety Laboratory in Virginia, points out, one of the effects of air-bags and seat-belts has been to reduce the number and severity of injuries to the head and chest – injuries which naturally used to have priority. Today, as he says, 'The lower limb is the most frequently injured body region. Approximately

10 per cent of all moderate to severe injuries occur in the foot and ankle region.'

When you analyse these injuries, he says, 'you find that most of the injuries are occurring in the right limb rather than the left limb. One of the differences that you notice between the right and left is the pedal controls: depressing the brake pedal is done with the right foot. So we've done a number of studies trying to look at how this interaction with the brake pedal might induce injury, and we've found that when the brake pedal is depressed or when the foot is on the brake pedal, there's a greater likelihood of instability because I've often got my foot up in the air and there can be rotation either outward or inward. The other observation we noted was that when I'm depressing the brake pedal, typically I do it with the musculature in my lower limb and I actually tend to raise my heel, so I'm lifting my heel up off the toe pin or floor pin, but then during a crash I cannot constrain myself, the forces are too great, so what happens is my foot comes down and will strike the toe pin very suddenly. What can happen then is, rather than getting these roll-type injuries, you can get an injury which is more like a compressive force under the bottom of the foot, which occurs when the heel strikes very suddenly.' It's worse for women and shorter drivers. They 'tend to lift their leg or their leg and heel higher, thereby creating a greater distance. The greater the distance the greater the risk of injury, so in our crash analyses we've found that shorter women also tend to be more commonly injured than male drivers.' As a result of such injuries he and the manufacturers are investigating putting padding on the toe pin structure of the pedal to reduce the force being transmitted to the ankle and the lower leg.

In very severe crashes, despite the introduction of 'crush spaces' front and back to absorb shocks, sometimes, as he says 'the toe pin can move into the occupant compartment – this is called intrusion. Since intrusion, this motion of crushing, increases the risk of injury, you would like to prevent intrusion into the vehicle, so several manufacturers are eliminating the intrusion through structural changes to the vehicle and through minor modifications to the toe pin region. Through padding and other counter measures, they're reducing the force transmitted when the foot strikes the toe pin.'

Changes like this are usually hidden from the driver – who may, however, still feel that the ever-increasing concern for safety is liable to take all the joy out of motoring. Not so, says John Telnack, Ford's senior designer. He points out that while 'some people feel that some of the fun has gone out [of driving] I think their definition of fun was just to go fast. I think that there's a lot more driving pleasure in the cars today because of their dynamics. We've improved the steering and the handling and the performance of the cars to a point today where the car really becomes an extension of the driver.

Seen in that light we've put more pleasure into driving, much more safety, so the driver has much more confidence in the vehicles that they're driving today. I think it's very easy to understand the difference today between cars of the fifties, which just went fast but didn't necessarily handle all that well, and cars today, which are designed to go fast, they're designed to handle well and to give performance on demand when you need it – for example, when you're overtaking on a highway, when you need the performance and when you need the steering capability to steer out of an emergency situation.'

In the end, of course, a car is only as safe as the sum of its parts, and among the most obviously important parts are the tyres. Today's radial tyres are infinitely safer and longer-lasting than they were even twenty years ago, but the very security they engender leads to negligence – especially if, as in Britain, laws are not as severe as they should be on worn tyres: the amount of tread that will pass muster is far less than most experts consider adequate. Moreover, as Rex Grogan, a leading tyre specialist, puts it, 'The big problem these days on the motorway, with modern vehicle suspensions, is that you simply don't know you've got a flat tyre, so it's very easy for people to let it go flat until they try to make a change of direction, usually it's an overtaking manoeuvre, and then they suddenly go out of control. Punctures happen much more frequently to rear tyres, which are the dangerous ones because the vehicle is inherently unstable. It's a bit like a bottle standing on its neck: it's all right if you leave it alone but you only want a tiny disturbing force and then it goes out of control. When the drama's all finished, somebody says, "Look at this tyre, a bad tyre, they don't make tyres like they used to." And the damage was done by a tiny little nail hole.' Wheel damage can also be caused by a tyre going flat because 'once the tyre is deflated then all the energy is concentrated on the wheel. The wheel will fold up quite readily, they're quite flimsy structures really, but when you put an inflated tyre on them they will absorb an enormous amount of energy.'

According to Grogan, 'There's nothing much we can do about punctures. There is a puncture-warning device coming, but it's still a few years off. Once we've got that then we can put some sort of alarm in the car and people will know when the tyre's beginning to go flat. Until then the only thing you can do is to listen – but do people listen? No, they just turn the sound up on the radio and try to drown the noise. There is a slight noise increase but it *is* only slight.' Saab, at least, recognizes the problem: it designs the rear axles of its cars to ensure that drivers get an early warning on corners in time to take corrective action if the tyres are about to lose their grip.

Before the puncture-warning device is in general use, tyres could be revolutionized by the use of Kevlar, a relatively new artificial fibre. This, as Grogan explains, 'will make a world of difference because out will go these nasty steel cords and with that the rust that plagues the steel-braced radial tyre. We'll have an all-textile tyre, lighter, stronger and no rust problems.' These are greater than anyone realizes. Grogan points to water, which is 'running along these very, very fine filaments of steel, rusting as it goes, until eventually the tyre becomes so weakened that it will fail just by an ordinary road. This is why Kevlar is such an exciting material because, being a textile, it doesn't suffer from rust, it keeps its strength even when it's wet, wonderful stuff.' The future also holds the promise of greater automation in tyre factories, which are still surprisingly labour-intensive. More automation will reduce the chance of badly made – above all, badly balanced – tyres.

In the meantime, the best answer is new tyres. As Grogan says: 'The only defence you've got against punctures is to have plenty of tread rubber. New tyres get punctures very much less frequently than worn tyres. On a badly worn tyre the accident rate increases sixty-fold so people who have frequent punctures are usually people who are running around on virtually bald tyres.'

In finding out what happens to a car's occupants in a crash one of the manufacturers' best weapons is the 'anthropomorphic test device', popularly known as the dummy, which they use in simulated crashes. Like so many elements in the safety story, these have a long history. As early as 1934 a test driver would stand on the running board of a new model at General Motors' proving ground and steer it down a hill into a wall of concrete blocks, jumping off just before the moment of impact. By the mid-1950s John Swearingen, a brilliant physiologist and head of the protection and survival laboratory at the Civil Aeronautical Research Institute, was using a small catapult capable of firing an object at up to 100 m.p.h., which sent dummies bearing instruments down a track to hit an aircraft seat. (The dummies had weird names like the Sierra 50, the VIP 50 and The Humanoid.) At much the same time, researchers at Wayne State University were using corpses to study the crash-proof qualities of different types of glass, and manufacturers were employing high-speed film analysis of cars containing dummies fitted with instruments. (The French, less squeamish than the Americans, were still using corpses in experiments.)

The modern, more realistic dummies were developed in Germany in the 1960s, as an element of a big programme of biomechanical research headed by Claude Tarrier. Dummies are now highly sophisticated, though researchers still have a major problem: crashes with dummies are expensive and few in number so they assume a head-on crash at 30 m.p.h. involving a thirty-year-old man of medium build, the so-called 50th percentile male. This creates two problems: it is clearly impossible to experiment with every possible shape assumed by car occupants; and the motor manufacturers are unwilling to test their models in the side-on collisions that are far more frequent.

The point has been taken on board, and Volvo, for instance, now has a whole family of dummies: the type used in their advertisements have now become cult objects. The family ranges from the standard male dummy they call 'Average Sam' to what they term a 'dainty little lady and a big strapping chap who is over six foot tall and weighs almost a hundred kilos'. Moreover, while the earlier models had only eleven measuring channels, the latest dummies have more than sixty, enabling the engineers to evaluate injuries to the whole body.

At the University of Virginia, Jeff Crandall refers to his dummies as 'my friends, my family'. According to him, 'The dummy has both several advantages and disadvantages. It's a very repeatable device, it can be used in many tests and give you the same results. It's very durable – it can be used over and over in these very severe crash tests and still come through with minimal damage and so it can be used again. But the differences between a dummy and a human are that obviously a dummy is not able to assess injury. What *can* be done with the dummy, however, is that you can try to predict injury, so that although the dummy is not injured you can measure things on it to try to predict injury, and you do this by having the dummies come in a variety of different sizes and they have a variety of different masses, heights and stiffnesses to try to re-create the human. If you have these different sizes and you put them in the vehicle and you have the stiffness and all the properties the same as a human, you hope that the dummy moves the same as a human would in a comparable crash condition.'

Today, researchers like Crandall are trying to go further, into what might be called micro-research into different parts of the body, especially the lower extremities. This creates problems. 'If you take my ankle, for example, you can see that it's rotating about a couple of axes in a fairly smooth and continuous motion. I can twist it in any direction. When we take the dummy we can see that we've got a similar motion and that we can twist it in any direction, but we see that it moves very easily until it hits the end and there's actually metal-to-metal contact in the dummy. What can happen if I'm using a dummy to try to predict a human response is that if this dummy is in a crash and the floor pin or the region underneath the pedals moves in and intrudes or structurally deforms, it can push against the foot and cause a very sudden acceleration or deceleration of the foot and cause it to hit metal to metal. It can get very sharp forces which are measured in the leg or tibia of the dummy, so one of the problems is that the resistance is not correct. The other thing you'll notice about the human is that there are some prescribed axes in the ankle for rotation – I have a much easier time going in some directions, twisting in some directions than in other directions. It's very difficult, for example, to roll my foot outward, called eversion, whereas if I roll my foot inward it's much easier, so these are not reflected in the dummy either. It's the same resistance in either direction.'

One of the primary limitations of a dummy as compared with a human foot, says Crandall, 'has to do with rotations in the ankle joint itself. In the dummy we have a ball joint, which allows it to rotate in any direction, but what we have in the human is a much more complex structure. We actually have twenty-eight bones that all come together and form a number of joints, so that any motion about the ankle joint is very complex.' Inevitably the complexities are not reflected in the dummy.

'What we're limited to in the dummy is to try to measure forces, accelerations and rotations, and to try to predict if injury would occur in the human. If the motion is not correct in the dummy then it is possible that we won't get the correct forces or the equivalent forces that would be measured in the human under the same test conditions. So, for example, if I try to push my foot to the side or I try to force my foot into outward rotation, I have a great deal of resistance here. However, in the dummy what we see is that I don't have any resistance until much later, so the foot of the dummy will respond differently than the foot of the human. Now, however, there is a new generation of dummies coming out that is trying to address this problem.'

It was not by chance that I quoted Volvo in the context of dummies: over the past sixty years the company has demonstrated conclusively – and emphasized the point in its advertisements with the early use of dummies crashing – that safety can be a selling point, and not only in cars sold to caring middle-class parents. Volvo was founded in 1927 to produce cars that imitated those produced in the United States. Within nine years, when everyone else in the world of motoring was talking exclusively in terms of 'the nut behind the wheel', in a sales manual Volvo's co-founder, Gustaf Larson, had laid down what was to be the company's credo: 'The fundamental principle of all design work is, and must be, safety. Each individual supporting part and component in the car must be dimensioned in such a way that it will withstand all forms of stresses and strains which it can be expected to be subjected to.'

By 1944, Volvo was already providing a 'safety cage' in the form of a stronger mid-section for the car, as well as such innovations as the laminated windscreen, and by 1954 it was providing an unprecedented five-year warranty in new cars – fiercely resisted by the country's insurers, who obviously felt that they would lose business. But its campaign for safer cars really started with the launch in 1956 of the Amazon, which included a number of safety-related innovations – for instance, the top half of the dashboard was properly padded.

Two years later, Gunnar Engellau, the company's dynamic chairman, took a decisive step by appointing Nils Bohlin, an engineer with experience in the safety aspects of aircraft design, to take charge of the safety side of Volvo's engineering. The first result of his appointment came with the introduction of the first modern-style seat-belts (also developed by the Swede, Birtil Aldman), replacing the historic lap-belts. According to Volvo, the first belt to resemble the present standard three-point model was designed by Herr Van Dobeln in 1952, although it had only one anchorage point, which was so low down that it imposed unnecessary strains on the driver. By the late 1950s, Volvo's engineers had designed a three-point belt, which was easy to use, comfortable, and provided effective protection. It was patented in 1958, introduced a year later as standard, a world first, and Volvo also pioneered the provision of belts for back-seat passengers. Since then the belts have been gradually improved with mechanical tensioners to provide maximum comfort and safety. Another improvement included the medically designed driver's seat, introduced in 1964.

(The industry's general attitude to car seats was expressed by an engineer from GM a few years later when I asked him why his company could not design a seat as comfortable and as supportive of the back as that in the – cheap – Renault 4. 'But that's a seat for a thousand-pound car in a six-hundred-pound vehicle.')

It was the Amazon's successor, the 144, introduced in 1966, which set the standard for safer cars the world over. It was deliberately designed to help the driver avoid accidents, while at the same time protecting the car's occupants in the event of a crash. Innovations included energy-absorbing crumple zones back and front, dual brake circuits, a steering column designed not to impale the driver in a crash, and safer 'anti-burst' door locks. Additional elements introduced in 1969 included head restraints on the front seats, rear seat-belts and electrically heated rear windows.

In 1972, to demonstrate that its concern for safety ran deep, Volvo produced an experimental safety vehicle as a mobile laboratory in which new features like anti-locking brakes and telescopic bumpers could be tested (most were later included in the 240–260 series). That same year, the company introduced rear-facing child seats – also introduced by Saab – bolted directly to the fixed car seat's under-frame. The seats had been designed in 1963 by Bertil Aldman, who had seen similar seats used for the astronauts in the American Gemini space capsule.

In 1976, Volvo's policy achieved official recognition when it was taken up by the American NHTSA as the benchmark against which the safety of other cars could be judged, which ensured that all other manufacturers were constantly embarrassed by the presence on their markets of cars officially classed as safer than their own. More recent improvements include detachable seats for children and the introduction in 1996 of a three-section collapsible steering column.

Among Volvo's other recent innovations have been side air-bags. These, known as the SIPS (Side Impact Protection System), are especially important not only because side-impact crashes are relatively numerous but because they are the object of less attention than head-on crashes, and because occupants are particularly exposed to injuries from even small side impacts – there is only the door between them and the impact.

The thinking behind SIPS and similar systems is explained by Jeff Crandall. In a side-impact crash, 'there are several interactions with the door and the incoming vehicle. Depending on the height at which the bumper contacts the door, the door can be pushed in, contact the pelvis and the lower limbs or the thigh region. The arm-rest can impact on the side of the occupant, his abdomen or chest, and then there is potential interaction with the head. If the car is being pushed out from under the occupant, the head can rotate over, and in some cases if the windshield breaks in very severe crashes the head can go out and actually strike the hood of the incoming vehicle. If it doesn't go outside the vehicle, it can strike the header region, up above the head on the windshield. We are trying to protect the torso and the head with side air-bags.'

The safety achievements of Saab have been rather overshadowed by those of Volvo, but they are not inconsiderable. Saab's cars were produced by a company that originally made aeroplanes, and was therefore more alert to safety considerations than pure motor manufacturers. The first Saab car, of 1949, already had front-wheel drive and a proper safety cage. By 1970 the company was fitting headlamp wipers and washers.

Today, Saab, like Volvo and, now, other manufacturers, design their car bodies in terms of the safety cage that houses the occupants with 'crumple zones' back and front, designed to absorb the shock of any collision as steadily as possible. Other Scandinavian pioneering efforts that have borne fruit elsewhere include daytime running lights. These, once Volvo's prerogative, are now widely recognized as an excellent method of saving lives by making it easier to detect on-coming vehicles. Another improvement is the high-mounted rear stop light, usually mounted just below a car's rear windscreen.

Nevertheless, and despite the way the manufacturers have been playing an admirable game of safety catch-up with their competitors, there remain astonishing discrepancies between the best and the worst vehicles. To take one startling example, a front-seat passenger in the four-door Chevrolet Corsica has a 44 per cent chance of life-threatening injuries in a crash, but only 6 per cent of the passengers in a Chrysler Sebring, a model of the same type and price, would suffer the same injuries. But Chrysler is by no means perfect: Nader's Raiders tracked down a design flaw in the door of one of the manufacturer's mini-vans, which led it to spring open on impact. Chrysler changed the design – but only after it had been threatened with exposure on television.

And there are still many faults waiting to be eliminated from many different cars: in the latest edition of his book, Nader provides a dozen examples, including better standards for such items as bumpers and head restraints. Moreover, the increasingly fashionable breed of utility vehicles, Multi-purpose Vehicles (MPVs) and four-wheel-drives, are liable to have a high centre of gravity, which makes them more likely to roll over – as did Mercedes' 'A-class' car.

Rather than grumble about the present, the veteran researcher Murray Mackay prefers to look at the future, when, according to him, 'We're going to see all sorts of improved crash performance coming along. We're going to see air-bags for side-impact protection, air-bags for roll-overs and to protect the lower limbs. We're going to see exterior protection to help pedestrians and cyclists, and intelligent variable restraint systems, so that they will be the appropriate restraint for either an elderly person or a husky young male. Really, we've just gone through chapter one of crash protection.'

As Saab points out, as compared to its first model, built less than fifty years ago, 'The number of functions that require manual controls has increased from twenty-three then to more than a hundred on today's Saab 900. The number of information messages to the driver has increased from nine to more than 150. The problem is compounded by spiralling traffic volumes and the more complex traffic environment.' Saab's solution is to improve the windscreen 'still the most important "display" and concentrate on arranging the dials and fascia so as not to overload the driver with impressions and signals, while ensuring that the information provided is 'relevant and easily understandable'. As one such attempt, Saab provides automatic climate control within the car.

This, of course, leads on to how far car improvements are self-destructive because they are liable to lull the driver into a dangerous lack of attention.

7

Roads to Nowhere

The story of the relationship between accidents and the condition of the road is well enough known. Better roads mean fewer accidents but more cars, leading to more accidents and ever-escalating demands for yet more roads. The whole vicious cycle can be summed up in a 1938 cartoon, drawn by the late Osbert Lancaster, of two planners (the lunacy of their ideas expressed by their exuberant hairstyles) looking at a map and declaring, 'Well, then, we must bypass the bypass.'

In 1938 the pioneers of grade-separated roads, the German autobahn and the American parkway, believed that they could build roads that were both safe and beautiful. And, indeed, until the 1970s they appear to resolve problems outside major cities: they were, and remain, far safer than roads where the traffic is not separated from pedestrians and from vehicles travelling in the opposite direction.

But the increased temptation to drive fast inevitably undermines some, though by no means all, of the advantages gained by the improvements. And it has taken until recently to accept that the idea of safe driving in towns and cities is a contradiction in terms, inevitably dangerous for other road users, above all pedestrians. The only answer, of course, is the separation of traffic, though not in the ways chosen in the first decades of post-war reconstruction, by giving priority to the motorist and relegating the pedestrian to a dirty underworld or an inconvenient upper level. Fortunately, today, enlightened road engineers like David Silcock accept that 'The town is a place for people, not a place for cars.' Earlier, less sophisticated, engineers believed that if there hadn't been an accident on a particular stretch of road, even in a town, it was safe.

You don't have to build completely new roads to tempt motorists: temptation comes with any improvement. 'The smoothness of a road has a great effect upon this sense of control and therefore upon the sense of safety,' says Gerald Wilde. 'If a road is uneven or full of potholes or very winding, you are continuously on your guard and you will have a stronger impression of the riskiness of the situation than when you're driving on an expressway with plenty of space and no unexpected curves. Studies have shown that for every foot wider you make a lane, people increase their speed by an average of about three miles per hour. The same thing holds for, say, edge markings: if there are clear edge markings along a road people will drive faster. Studies have indicated that sometimes improved edge markings lead to an increase of the accident rate of the road in question, so the road itself gives you information that enters into this intuitive risk calculation and controls your behaviour.'

Yet the idea that better roads resulted in fewer accidents was, and remains, perfectly sensible. In the past, the control, and indeed the elimination of, infectious disease has been due to improvement of the environment through the provision of pure water and proper sewerage. The same is true of roads. As Murray Mackay put it in his 1972 report on road accidents in the *International Journal of Environmental Studies*, 'In an academic sense, one may say that any environment which allows two vehicles to collide with each other is deficient.'

The early researchers found, in Murray Mackay's words, that 'There were lots of "covert" environmental deficiencies that only came out from detailed study, things like curvatures, surfaces, camber, street-lighting, that sort of thing.' They discovered that engineers had been concerned only with what happened on the road itself and had not taken into account that the majority of single-vehicle accidents involved hitting objects that were off the road. According to Murray Mackay, about a third of car occupants who die 'do so when their cars leave the road and strike roadside objects such as lamp-posts, trees, telegraph poles and the like. Such collisions occur quite predictably on bends with unfavourable cambers, low coefficient road surfaces, poor or zero lighting and against objects close to the roadway edge, set at the approach or on the apex of a bend.'

But, inevitably, with improvement comes improvidence. Bernhard Potter points out how 'in East Germany, after the country was reunited, people started to say, "We have to cut down all those trees along the roads because we get off the roads and people die." Nobody said, "We have to get cars that are safer," or "We have to drive slower." What they wanted to do was cut down all those trees and build streets where you don't have curves, basically autobahns.' At that point it is difficult to disagree with Bob Davis's resigned attitude: 'If you create an idiot-proof situation for the motorist, by giving him or her a road which it's extremely easy to drive on, with barriers down the middle so you don't have to worry about going on the wrong side of the road, cutting trees down beside the road so you don't have to worry about driving off it, you will tend to produce idiots.'

Engineers have also come to grips with the danger presented by roadside furniture and are steadily improving lamp-posts, billboards and bollards, as well as such picturesque but dangerous elements as overhanging trees – for the normal type of furniture is designed to kill. After all, says Murray Mackay, 'A telegraph pole, a lamp-post or even a tree no more than five inches in diameter is an essentially rigid object, totally unyielding to a car's structure at 30 m.p.h. or so. The result is an extremely hostile impact, often causing crushing of the passenger compartment and serious injury. These are predictable events for which technical solutions have been known for twenty years. In the early 1970s, the Department of Transport's own research laboratory developed breakable joints for the base of a lamp-post; in Sweden, thin-walled steel lamp standards fold and curl when struck by a car, cushioning the collision; in the United States and Australia, careful weakening of the base of wooden telegraph poles allows them to shear off when struck by a car yet still have a normal in-service performance.' In Britain, the city of Birmingham has done a great deal to minimize the shock of impact with pillars, supports and columns by using a 'crash cushion' in front of the structures to provide a couple of metres of what Mackay calls 'ride-down' to soften the impact – an idea, amazingly, opposed by the Department of Transport.

Indeed, Britain is backward in trying to improve the roadside environment. Even the minor improvements that could do so much to improve road safety are impeded by the ridiculous rules imposed by the Treasury. The savings that could be made, in terms of the cost of fatalities and injuries, are calculated, but only schemes showing the ludicrously high rate of return of 50 per cent are considered. And, notably unlike every country in continental Europe, no attempt has been made in towns to reduce the number of poles at the roadside. The rules ensure a maximum of rigid, dangerous columns for traffic-lights, which are often not even placed to provide a proper view of the lights for drivers.

(Not that traffic-lights themselves are an ideal solution. They were introduced in the 1930s by engineers in the United States and later in many other countries as a safety device. 'Their history as a safety device,' says Gerald Wilde, 'has been studied over and over again. What you see after the installation of a traffic-light is a change in the type of accident occurring. You have fewer collisions at ninety degrees, because the right of way has been clearly assigned in a temporary fashion. But what you get is more left-turn [in the USA; right turn in the UK] accidents, more rear-enders. This is not surprising because as you are approaching a traffic-light, perhaps driving in front of me, you see that light changing from green to amber and you decide to stop. I see the same change but I figure I can just make it before the light turns red. So we have a rear-end collision because we are interpreting the situation in different ways. The upshot is that traffic-lights change the type of accidents but not their number, or even their severity.

Rear-end collisions can be very severe in terms of whiplash. With traffic-lights you improve traffic flow, but not safety.')

Today, engineers have lost many of their illusions. 'We used to think that building a bypass solved a town's traffic problem,' says David Silcock, the theory being that 'you take away some of the traffic from the town, put it on the bypass and everything's fine. It isn't like that. The traffic that remains can go faster, accident rates can increase and there have been examples where that has happened. The way we try to get round that now is by putting traffic-calming measures in the town centre on the old bypass routes.'

'Traffic calming' involves the artificial narrowing of streets and creating bumps – while trying at the same time not to make them too steep, hence the increasing fashion for the less effective but generally more acceptable flat bumps instead of the older rounded type. 'Traffic calming' is an unsatisfactory solution for two obvious reasons: the devices may calm the traffic but they do nothing to calm the drivers, who may be infuriated by them. And calming traffic implies that it will still be allowed into the centre of towns, from which it should, of course, be banned.

Nevertheless, as in so many other aspects of safety, roads are improving and attitudes changing, though not fast enough to satisfy onlookers. 'When I trained as a young engineer,' says Silcock, 'road-design standards were absolute and they were often argued on grounds of safety. If you make a bend less steep you offer a safety benefit. Over the years we have learnt that if you make the bend less sharp drivers go around it faster so some of that safety benefit gets taken up by higher speed. As engineers we need to understand how road-users react to the facilities we're providing, and I think that is the change of attitude that is now happening in the profession.'

Engineers are now prepared to listen to psychologists about the effect the changes they make to roads will have on drivers' behaviour. 'Engineers never really thought about psychologists,' says Silcock. 'Psychology was something that happened in the laboratory or in advertisements. It wasn't something that was relevant to an engineering design. We didn't really think about how people interacted with the facilities we were providing. Those at the architectural and planning end of the community, perhaps, but those at the hard engineering end, particularly the road designers, took very little account of the way in which road-users and the machines that were using the road were changing and responding to the facilities being provided.' But now 'engineers and psychologists are beginning to work together to try and understand these problems. But it's a slow process, we are all defensive of our professional position and one of the difficulties has been the engineering community taking on board the lessons that other disciplines can tell us. That is now happening but it's been a long process.'

Changing the mind-sets of motorists, finance ministries and road engineers takes time, and in the meantime people are dying, and mistakes are still being made. In Britain, at least, there seems to be no urgency and no imagination in actually tackling the dilemmas inevitably posed by the design of roads. Yet, surely, the rules are simplicity itself: as far as traffic and pedestrians are concerned, outside towns separation is all, while within urban areas the pedestrian should be king.

8

Drivers Are Only Human, After All

You can't blame the vehicle and you can't blame the highway and the only factor left to consider is the driver and it's drivers who are the problem on the road.

Steve Stradling, psychologist

Murray Mackay considers that in 90 per cent of accidents there is some form of human error, 'in about 50 per cent there's something wrong with the highway design and only in about 5 or 6 per cent is there some contribution from the car'.

One of the biggest problems is that there are, relatively speaking, so few accidents. 'If a Martian anthropologist was suspended fifty miles up in the air observing the movement of road traffic,' says Steve Stradling, a psychologist at the Driver Behaviour Research Group at Manchester University, 'certainly in the UK and probably in most other countries as well, they'd be amazed that there are so few crashes rather than that there are so many. In some ways human beings ought to be congratulated for adapting to and handling the demands of the situation as well as they do. As a result, notes Leonard Evans, principal research scientist at General Motors' Research and Development Center in Michigan, 'The typical driver has a crash about once every ten years and if you're doing something that only leads to something bad once every ten years, the normal explanation is that you were very unlucky, that the other guy did something he shouldn't have. Very few would interpret this as a natural and inevitable outcome of average driving, especially as most crashes involve only damage to property. Injury crashes are much less frequent, and fatalities occur to drivers, statistically speaking, once per four thousand years.'

Matters are not improved by the general assumption that everyone else on the road is sane, sober and competent. 'When you look at vehicle design and highway design and the wide range of drivers that are licensed and put

117

out on the road,' says Dr Pat Waller, of the Michigan Transportation Research Institute, 'The amazing thing is that crashes are as infrequent as they are.' Steve Stradling reinforces this view: 'Somebody once said to me that driving on a motorway is like flying in formation with complete strangers. What you need to be able to do is to predict what others are likely to do because the predictability of other drivers is the cornerstone of road safety, and if you're flying in formation with complete strangers at high velocity, well, you're on a wing and a prayer there, aren't you?'

As a result, to most drivers a lack of accidents equals safety. 'There's a process,' observes Dr Bob Gunther, a psychologist at the Rehabilitation Institute of Michigan in Detroit, 'whereby people form attitudes based on what they're doing. They observe themselves doing something and infer meaning from it. If I'm driving 85 m.p.h. then this must be a very safe thing to do. Smokers do the same thing every day: when a smoker lights a cigarette and observes themselves smoking they say to themselves, "This must not be that dangerous for me or I wouldn't be doing it." [Similarly] a driver operating a motor vehicle at a high rate of speed will look at their own behaviour and infer from it a number of things: I must be a very skilful driver and this must be very safe for me.'

And when people see a crash, why, for sure, it isn't going to happen to them, not according to Dr Gunther, anyway. 'There's a way of thinking that insulates us from our own frailties. It's very common. When we see a bad thing happen to somebody else we assume it happens to them because of something they have done, because of something about them. When a bad thing happens to us, to me, I assume that it's because of something outside of me, some force, some power, some enemy that I was unable to overcome, it's never my fault. So when I see other people injured in a terrible crash, I assume it's their fault, they caused it to happen to themselves but that will never happen to me because I won't make that mistake, and after having weaved my way through the traffic jam and getting by the ambulances, I then breathe a sigh of relief, floor the accelerator and speed away at 80 m.p.h.'

The reasons as to why we are dangerous on the road stem from why we buy a car in the first place. Daniel McCarthy, a road safety officer in Devon, thinks that 'We buy cars to reflect what we believe are decisions we can make about our lifestyle. Marketing men tell us a car says things about us that mere clothes or where we live or what we do or what colour credit cards we have could never say. What I drive is what I am and the car will imbue me with a sense of power, of control, of ability, of intelligence, of charm, of sexual vigour that I may or may not possess but they're certainly attributes that I think I can buy myself into. I think that the element of our personality that very often gets developed by the car is a very immature, a very selfish part of ourselves, possibly prone to moodiness and bouts of depression. It's a part of ourselves that craves attention, that demands respect and gives none to others and cares little for others and is cruel to animals and unfair to people. I think the person we are at risk of becoming behind the wheel is the sort of person we wouldn't really want to take home to our mothers.'

Inevitably, too, the way we drive, Steve Stradling feels, says a lot about us. It 'involves saying "I'm the kind of person who follows rules quite happily" or "I'm the kind of person who doesn't get exercised or worked up or irritated by what other people are doing" or it involves saying, "Hey, out of my way, I need special access, priority, that's my bit of space, I was there first, I saw it first, that's mine." '

What makes us even more dangerous on the road is our excessive belief in our own capacities. Recent studies have merely confirmed what we already instinctively knew, that three-quarters of us think that we are better than other drivers. In crashes, inevitably, four out of five of us blame the other – and only about 5 per cent of drivers admit to being below average. Moreover, says Leonard Evans, drivers 'observe the foolish things that other people do, they tend to not observe the foolish things they do themselves because if they observed them they wouldn't do them. One can easily notice that other driver who forgot to cancel a turn signal but when you've forgotten to cancel *your* turn signal you often do not notice even until you make the next turn and it gets cancelled.'

Evans goes on: 'Experience is a very bad teacher in this area. Who would fly with a commercial airline if all the pilot knew was what he had learnt by experience? That is, that he would land and that he would have a following wind: experience had taught him this was OK, meaning he'd never crashed before. The very safe system of aviation is that way because everyone who is flying a commercial airline is expected to conform to what is a more general collective experience where the pilot is benefiting from everybody's experience that is codified into certain advice and requirements.'

Inexperience is compounded by many other factors, identified over the past half century by many psychologists and sociologists. Most obviously, driving appeals to our primitive lust for power. For driving, says John Whitelegg, Professor of Environmental Studies at John Moores University, Liverpool, 'is liberation, freedom, mastery, control, sexual excitement. It's power over things and power over other people, and for many people it will be the only excitement they get in a day. The only marginal increase in adrenaline all day is going to be the twenty-minute drive to work and the twenty-minute drive home, so drivers are going to behave in a way where they get maximum pleasure from the driving experience.' But, as Daniel McCarthy, a road safety officer in Exeter, says, there's also a touch of bitterness: after we've bought 'into this myth of limitless personal freedom at the turn of a key, all we've got is an opportunity to join an unending traffic queue full of fumes'.

Nevertheless commuters cherish these moments. In New York, where the cost of driving is two or three times that of public transportation, a survey conducted for the Port of New York Authority a couple of years ago by Larry Zeitlin, a psychologist, found that 'most people enjoy the convenience, the privacy, they are willing to put up with the inconvenience of driving for the pleasure that the drive gives them, the radio, smoking, chatting with people, singing at the top of their lungs. It's about the only time most people are alone during the day, it's difficult to be truly alone, certainly in the New York area.'

The most obvious, and the most dangerous, symptom of the undesirable character traits we reveal when driving is that of excessive speed, the ultimate expression of the primitive need for power – and, of course, the higher the speed the higher the high (a point proved most recently by observations from the Nottingham Road Accident Unit). Not surprisingly, excessive speed remains by far the biggest single element in crashes and, above all, ensures that crashes will cause the maximum damage to the people involved. 'At 30 m.p.h. it's possible that a child could be killed or an adult could be killed when struck by a car,' says Sergeant Mike Doyle. 'At 40 m.p.h. it's highly likely, and at 50 m.p.h. it's almost certain.'

This makes the association of fast cars with drink all the more unfortunate. The Indianapolis 500, the premier motor race in the United States, is a prime example. 'We have the cars racing on the track with logos on the sides advertising beer,' says Dr Pat Waller, 'and then we're surprised that young people associate beer with driving. We know that for drunk-driving crashes in general, not just for young people, beer is the beverage that accounts for something over 80 per cent of them and young people are very vulnerable in this regard.'

Despite the introduction of ever more strict drink driving regulations, there are still too many people who, if not drunk in charge of this 'big powerful object', find that their reflexes, the speed of their reactions, are affected by drink, which leads them to compound their problems by driving too fast. 'The highest majority of accidents involving drink also involve speed,' says Mike Doyle. 'People become casual and not aggressive but feel capable of doing all sorts of things when they've been drinking and that's when they have problems because they can't react quite so quickly. We can't determine the fact that they've reacted in a particular way because of drink but investigating the accident we can corroborate evidence of drink because of strange things that happen to the vehicles or the strange way in which the accident happens.

'I dealt with an incident where fortunately the people were injured only slightly, but when I looked at the vehicle I expected to be taking bodies out. The vehicle had approached a wide open island and left skid marks somewhere in the region of 35 to 40 metres long and skidded straight across the island and hit the central raised section. If it had been travelling perhaps a little more quickly or the driver hadn't suddenly realized that he was approaching an island, there was a 30- to 40-foot drop on the other side of the concrete wall and we would have certainly been dealing with fatalities then. But, more importantly, he or I or anybody could have been driving around that island perfectly innocently and could have been involved in that accident.

'Now that driver was more than three times over the legal limit on drink, and his female passenger was injured quite badly on her knees, scarred for life, and that's a slight injury accident in our terms. Somebody is scarred for life – it's not a slight injury but in purely statistical terms it's slight.'

With speed goes aggression, for the driver's mind-set is often that of a soldier in charge of a deadly weapon: the accelerator is the trigger, the steering wheel the sights on the barrel, and because the victims are hidden inside their cars they are, like opposing forces on the battlefield, simply depersonalized enemies. The aggression may even be personal, says Steve Stradling. Interpersonal hostility ranges 'all the way from beeping your horn and making gestures with or without fingers at other road-users, threatening gestures, up to using your vehicle to retaliate against other road-users by driving close up behind them or pushing into spaces, taking up road space and denying that to other drivers and, in the extreme, occasionally using your car to chase after other drivers, screeching to a halt in front of them, leaping out with a tyre lever in your hand and making physical threats. Unfortunately that seems to be on the increase.'

He's not exaggerating. One (inevitably anonymous) motorcycle courier in New York sees it as open war: 'Cab drivers, they're on commission so they try to jump in front, try to cut each other's throats because they have to get more passengers so they can make more money. Bikers, we get along, you know. We know we are here with no protection and we try not to hurt each other but it's like us against them, the truck drivers, the bus drivers, especially the bus drivers. They're more crazy because I guess they have more insurance, more protection, you know, they have more back-up . . . and they'll win, put it like that, the bus drivers will win. Cab drivers, they know if they hit us they've got to pay. The regular people, they just come out here to the city, try to drive, they don't understand this so then they'll just get upset and, you know, they'll start arguing with us and stuff like that.'

This atmosphere of menace represents a Hobbesian view of life. As Daniel McCarthy says, 'We've bought into the myth of cheap personal transport, society is on the move, we are in motion. We're driving up and down life's highway, honking our horns and waving our fists at our fellow travellers, so it's a kind of club. It's a fairly dog-eat-dog world – they're all competing for the same diminishing resources and road space and that puts them pretty well up there as, I suppose, antagonists or even enemies in some readings of the situation' – including McCarthy's own. On a bad day: 'It seems very often the prevailing atmosphere is one of intimidation and aggression, one where any mistake is seized upon very seriously by those around you and interpreted as a personal threat against them.'

Within this Hobbesian world, there isn't much room for pleasure, according to some theorists. 'I suppose we all buy into a dream that driving is pleasurable', says McCarthy, 'and there are moments that sustain us, I'm sure. Driving is, indeed, a pleasurable activity when the road is empty and you're not under stress to be somewhere five minutes ago and there's not some tractor in front of you slowing you down to fifteen miles an hour. But I have to say on the whole driving is not a pleasurable activity. I think you can look at the levels of stress in drivers' faces – stand at a set of traffic-lights and look at the general expressions as people drive past you, their hands are clenched, their faces are looking grim, they're frowning, they've got furrowed brows.'

But there are those, like Csaba Csere, editor-in-chief of the American magazine *Car & Driver*, who believe that driving can be pleasurable and that this is not incompatible with the increased safety built into cars. His readers, he says, 'are interested in safety but they're primarily interested in having fun with cars. Our readers are triple-distilled car lovers, they're people who really like the act of driving and what they're primarily interested in is enjoying automobiles and learning as much about them as they possibly can.' Despite the increased costs imposed by safety requirements, 'There are some parts of safety that are totally compatible with what our readers are interested in, active safety. The notion of avoiding accidents rather than simply surviving them requires a car that has very good handling, that has good brakes and those are, of course, the sort of things that driving enthusiasts are looking for, for driving pleasure as well, so those are perfectly compatible.'

As Csere says, safety may be perfectly compatible with the undoubted pleasures of speeding, but accidents do happen. Stradling's group has identified 'three main kinds of bad or aberrant behaviours on the road that we call lapses, errors and violations. Firstly lapses: these are embarrassing but not dangerous, and they're things like trying to pull away from the traffic-lights in the wrong gear or hitting the wrong switch on the dashboard, forgetting where you left the car in the car park. Next up are errors and those are things like failing to see a stop or give-way sign, misjudging an overtaking gap, braking too hard for the conditions, not noticing cyclists coming up on your near-side and errors of observation or errors of judgement. The third sort, the most important, are what we call violations and these are doing naughty things on the road, all the way from speeding, which is the most frequent, through to drink-driving which is nowadays the least frequent, but also covering things like tail-gating, getting up too close behind the driver in front, running through red traffic-lights just as they change, showing hostility to other road-users. We think there are psychologically quite different motivations, and mechanisms behind lapses, errors and violations. and what we've found in our research is that if we ask people, "How many accidents have you had in the last three years?", it isn't lapses that predict accidents and it isn't errors that predict accidents. No, it's violations, so in that sense it's naughty drivers who are most likely to be crash involved.

'The kinds of people who are most likely to be crash involved are people who have a bad attitude towards driving, who break rules and regulations. Now, it's not necessarily the case that they're violating when they have an accident but they're the kind of person who is more likely to be involved in a crash. So we think the basic equation is violation plus error equals crash, and in that order, somebody who drives in a risky, reckless, disregarding sort of manner, plus them or another driver making an error of judgement or observation, that's when a crash happens.

'At the moment most violators, if they think about it at all, think that what they're doing is socially acceptable because, they'll say, "Well, everybody else does it, don't they?" In point of fact, when we looked more closely we found that they say that everybody else does it but they're over-estimating the number of other people who do it, so they're using that as their justification but they're not strictly correct [when] they're using that as a sufficient excuse for doing it themselves.'

Part of the problem is simply that the risk appears so low. This, as Alison Smiley says, 'makes people feel safe, and for the most part they are, but they're taking risks. We frequently experience a period of inattention, you know, you're driving home from work, you've been on this route a thousand times, you meant to go to the dry cleaner, which meant turning at such and such a corner, but you start thinking about something and you're on automatic pilot and, zap, you're right through the intersection before you know it, you've been inattentive. That's a very typical event for a driver.

'Sometimes that inattention results in something that's a little more exciting, like you accidentally go through a stop sign. Most drivers have had that experience where they weren't paying attention as they approach an intersection. They go through a stop sign, get to the other side and their heart starts pounding. But they were lucky, there were no cars crossing at that time and that's why accidents are rare events, because when you make these errors the circumstances are favourable to you, there just doesn't happen to be any traffic crossing at that precise instant.'

Modern cars, ever quieter, accentuate this tendency to inattention. Unfortunately, as Steve Stradling says, people 'feel as safe and snug as in a womb. They're lulled by the cocoon effect. Cars are getting more and more comfortable, more and more relaxing. You can now do all sorts of other things, you can listen to music, you can listen to the radio, you can take phone calls, you can dictate memos, so the driver is getting more and more removed from the outside environment.' Worse, says Siamack Salari, a researcher at J. Walter Thompson, the advertising agency, 'we actually go into a kind of auto-pilot. Journeys that we make regularly such as taking the kids to school or going to the local supermarket, up to two or three miles, we can do quite easily without even remembering how we got there. So we'll get to our destination and we won't remember all the traffic, lights we went through, the junctions, the cars that overtook us, the pedestrians who we allowed to cross on the way.'

Under those circumstances, as transport consultant David Silcock puts it, 'It's very easy to forget the vulnerable road-users, the pedestrians and the cyclists. I'm safe in the car, therefore the other people tend to be forgotten or not perceived in the same way. We may be transferring the risk from me in the car to other road-users outside it.'

The veteran motorist and ex-car salesman Lord Lucas says: 'I think there is a real danger in a modern motor-car, with its air-conditioning, with its in-car entertainment, its telephone and so on and so forth, isolating the driver from the real world outside. I think therefore that you can't make it into a "sitting room on wheels". It's a piece of machinery and it's got to be treated as such, with care, with respect.'

With driving, as with virtually every other human activity, familiarity breeds contempt – and inattention. 'The problem with driving all the time,' says Alison Smiley, 'is that it's very difficult to pay continuous attention to what you're doing. Driving becomes an automated task, like tying your shoelaces or playing the piano – you don't really have to pay attention to it all the time. Everybody's had the experience of listening to a speech or a sermon or whatever and they feel they ought to be paying attention, and they try consciously to focus their attention on it, but inevitably their mind starts to wander and they have to pull it back, so it's not a trainable capacity that we have and it's one that ends up in accidents frequently.'

Worse, says Stradling, if drivers 'are in a stressed state and need to concentrate because the demands are high, then anything that encourages them to relax too much and feel too secure and too comfortable is going to slow down their reaction times and encourage them to reduce their safety margins and going to make them more dangerous to themselves and to other drivers.' And worse still, says Daniel McCarthy, is their 'belief in their invulnerability. They have so completely allowed themselves to inhabit their metal bodies that they don't fear death, they are oblivious of the fact that even in very minor collisions they face a four out of five risk of serious injury. They're oblivious of the fact that anybody foolhardy enough to step into their path at the sort of speeds they will generally drive at through residential areas is 85 per cent likely to sustain fatal injury. The truth is, they are so entranced by the myth of themselves as drivers that they are not aware of just how easily life can be extinguished, both within the car and obviously outside.'

This unawareness is truly terrifying. As the psychologist Conrad King remarks: 'Feeling no fear when we drive is one of the big contributing factors to accidents. If people were fully aware of the consequences of what goes wrong on the roads, you'd never have people driving three inches off someone else's bumper, you'd never have people cutting each other up in traffic, so the sense of distance that we get from other drivers and the sense of protection and invulnerability that we get from the car really turns us into quite dangerous people. We're people who feel like we're not going to get hurt and we're in charge of a big powerful object.'

Aggression, power, increasing frustration add up to that most typical of modern problems: road rage. In the end, says the American Automobile Association, 'We may very well discover that personal frustration, anger and testosterone are the most dangerous drugs on the highway.'

'Driving's getting more stressful in two ways,' says Steve Stradling. 'There's greater mental load: you have to concentrate harder, there are more things happening and they're happening faster and faster so that's taxing. It's also emotionally stressful: as well as the demands increasing, things that can be interpreted as threatening happen more and more often, so driving is getting to be a strain and a pain.'

Conrad King lists a frightening number of the types of stress to which a driver is subject: 'The stress from other road-users, people cutting you up, driving too close. Whether it's outside stress from normal living, needing to get to an appointment, the stress you bring with you in terms of arguments, what happens is that there's a number of these stresses that a driver faces. Stress raises your heart-rate, blood pressure and endorphin levels, which means that you're going to react to situations a lot more, so when you're actually confronted with a minor stressful incident on the road, you've already had enough so your reaction can be completely out of proportion. So if somebody drives a little bit too close to you, you've got all of the stress in your body and you want to lash out to take away the thing that's causing you stress – and what you have to lash out with is a car.'

The result, according to the recent research at Manchester University, has been the division of violations into three major types. Stradling calls them: 'maintaining progress, gaining advantage, and inter-personal hostility. In maintaining progress, you want to keep going so anything that slows you down, roundabouts, junctions, traffic-lights, other traffic, people cutting in front of you, people in your space, is going to increase your stress levels, making you more irritable and more angry. When people are angry they don't drive as well as they ought to and there may be other consequences as well. Gaining advantage is about winning the small battles on the road, those small victories of which daily life is composed and about which you can boast to your pals in the pub at the end of the day – somebody you cut up, somebody you got away faster than, somebody who you overtook when they weren't looking, the small victories that add that necessary bit of pleasure to one's daily existence.

'The third aspect, in many ways the most worrying, is showing hostility to other road-users. This is gesticulating, with or without fingers, and worse than that, using your car to threaten other drivers, either by getting close up behind or getting into a space and denying that space to other people. At the extreme you get road rage where people chase after other drivers and screech to a halt in front of them and leap out and make physical threats.'

Road rage can also, says Bernhard Potter, a German journalist, result when 'the car is considered by many people an extension of their private sphere, so basically you're not leaving your home, you're taking your living room with you to work. I think that's also a reason why a lot of people tend to act very aggressively once their cars get damaged, even if there is only minor damage on their car. We had an incident where the people got so mad at each other that they threatened each other with guns on the autobahn while driving, and I think that has something to do with "You're preventing me from doing what I want to do." '

Of course, as with any new phenomenon, road rage can be blamed for every problem. As Csaba Csere points out: 'The head of the National Highway Traffic and Safety Administration recently claimed that there's 28,000 traffic fatalities a year caused by road rage. Given that this is 70 per cent of the total traffic fatalities in the US this seems to be an amazing number. When you get down to his definition of road rage, he's basically lumped virtually every traffic offence, speeding, drinking while driving, inattentive driving, cursing at other drivers in addition to pure road rage, under this category and I think what we're seeing is an attempt on the part of the safety agencies and the law-enforcement agencies to come up with a justification for heavy traffic enforcement now that "Speed kills" no longer holds up – given the record that we saw from '95 to '96 when speed limits were increased.' (See page 140.)

Indeed, in many ways, road rage is a new word for an old problem. Steve Stradling recounts how Lord Byron 'had an altercation with another carriage driver whom he thought had cut him up on the road. So carriage rage was known about a couple of hundred years ago, and I think there's always been anger and aggression and frustration and irritation on the roads.

'It may just be that there's something about the car, that these aren't just people who are driving as they live. Certainly, there are some people who get exercised when they're off the road and attempt to exact retribution but it looks as if there are also some people who are mild-mannered and polite and forgiving when they're out of their car and maybe there's something about being in the car that brings down barriers, perhaps because there's a poor communication system. If you do something bad there aren't easy ways to say you're sorry and if two of the wrong sorts of people get involved in this kind of traffic conflict, then it can escalate.'

This brings in the concept of driving as a form of warfare. 'Most people,' says Conrad King, 'don't think of themselves as killers, yet when a country goes to war, a significant proportion of the population is capable of killing. When we're driving what happens is that we're in a protected environment. When someone invades our space the part of our brain that deals with reacting to threat perceives it as a threat to our lives. There are two ways of dealing with a threat: one, you can run away, two, you can try to kill or destroy the thing that's threatening you. What happens with driving is you can't run away so our brain, or the primitive part of our brain, thinks that the only response is to take away the threat. So you're driving, someone cuts you up, you respond aggressively and that's where you get an escalation of violence and aggression on the roads. You only need to get it wrong once on the road to kill someone. Many drivers never get it wrong but most drivers on the road are potential killers.'

This brings King back to the idea of the car as a weapon: 'If you put a gun in somebody's hands you're going to change their personality, you're going to affect what they are capable of. If you put someone behind the wheel of a car it's exactly the same. First of all, they're capable of going at 100 m.p.h., which they never would without the car, but also they're capable of destroying somebody, crushing someone, whipping them to pieces just by a little move of the wheel. Now that's giving someone a weapon, that's giving them a lot more potential for destruction than they would ever have in their own physical body.'

The situation is not entirely hopeless. Conrad King works with people who've had problems with violent and aggressive driving styles. 'These are people who have either lost their temper when they're driving, have been involved in accidents or even been involved in physical assaults on other motorists. I work with them, looking at their attitudes towards driving, what their expectations are before they get in the car. I also encourage them to look at what the potential consequences might be of getting something wrong, so instead of – well, say you have an accident, the car's written off, I get them to go through something like this scenario: you have an accident in which you are killed, who notifies your family, what are going to be the emotional consequences for the people around you, what are going to be the financial consequences for the people around you, what about all of the aspects of your life that you haven't had a chance to tie up, what about all the aspects of your life that haven't been completed, and I push to quite a deep emotional level so that they are fully aware of the consequences of getting it wrong when they're driving.

'I also get people to look at their driving skills and their driving style, so that if people drive in a defensive style and keep a lot of space around the car, then it means they're a lot less likely to react badly to someone else's mistake on the roads. That means that they've got plenty of time and they can just keep themselves safe. Part of the dehumanization that goes on with driving is that we don't view ourselves as humans and we don't place the appropriate value on ourselves. Now, if we have to transport someone we love, a child, we'll make sure that they're safe, we'll make sure that they're not put at risk. Yet we'll take enormous risks with the father of that child or the mother of that child. If it's ourselves and we don't think of the consequences, this child will lose a parent because we don't feel human when we drive, because we're part man, part machine, part of the freeway.'

But the problems faced by drivers, and the people they encounter on the road, are not by any means entirely subjective. 'People are very limited in how well they perceive closing velocity,' says Alison Smiley, 'how well they can tell how rapidly a car is coming towards them, and the net result of that is that when you're in an overtaking situation you assume that the car coming towards you is going about the speed of the traffic stream and you base your timing on that assumption. If it so happens that that car is travelling a whole lot faster, you're not going to realize that until you're close enough to it for it to become an extremely hazardous situation. Overtaking is a guessing game: you can't know at what speed that oncoming car is coming, you can't perceive it until you're so close you can't do anything about it, so you've got to time your pass and your speed according to assumptions about what that oncoming car is going to be doing and if your assumptions are wrong, you're in trouble.

'Our field of view is very broad. We can see 90 degrees to the left, 90 degrees to the right, slightly less above and below, but the area in which we can see accurately is actually very small, it's about the size of a quarter [or a 10p piece] held at arm's length. That means that if we want to see something well enough to tell whether the light has changed, or the pedestrian's going to change their mind and move in a different direction, or the oncoming car is moving more quickly than we want it to be, then we have to look directly at it and that means that drivers search the scene in front of them in a series of very brief fixations. They look at the pedestrian, say, and then zap over to the traffic-light – zap over to the car that's coming towards them – and during the time it takes to make each of these fixations, the car travels a considerable distance.'

At night things are worse. 'We know,' says Alison Smiley, 'that a driver on low-beam headlights is not going to be able to see a dark object at very great distance so that if the driver is going at more than about thirty-five miles per hour they're not going to be able to stop in time for a pedestrian in a dark coat who suddenly steps out in front of them. That's an inevitable kind of accident. We rely too much on our headlights at night and yet we still have speed limits of 50 m.p.h. on real roads [in the USA; in the UK 70 m.p.h.] where we can have these kinds of accidents.'

Our brain, like our eyes, also has its limitations: it can take in only so much information at a time, and on the road it suffers from information overload, especially at what Smiley calls intersections and the British would term crossroads. 'The problem for the driver,' she says, 'is that he or she has got to do a lot of different things at once. If we consider, for example, the driver who's making a left turn [in the USA; a right turn in the UK] against oncoming traffic, that driver is very busy as they're approaching the traffic-light. First of all, they've got to keep an eye on the car in front of them. If that car suddenly slows and they're not watching it, they can end up in a rear-end accident. Secondly, they've got to keep an eye on the traffic-light, if it turns caution [amber] they might want to hurry up and get through the intersection. If it turns red they don't want to be entering the intersection. Thirdly, they've got to keep an eye on cars in the lanes beside them, who might suddenly move over in front of them, realize this is the intersection where they meant to make the turn and decide they've got to do it now. Fourthly, they've got to keep an eye out for pedestrians crossing against them. They're going to cross the path of pedestrians, and pedestrians that they can see easily in front of them and pedestrians that are going to be behind them as they approach the intersection. Finally, they have to keep an eye on where they're going: when you get to the intersection all the lane markings disappear and you've got to select the proper road path through the intersection so you track down the lane properly. You've got a whole lot of different things that you're doing as you approach this turn and unfortunately we're only really capable of doing one thing well at a time. We do things serially one after the other.'

I came to this book with the firm belief, which was backed – to some extent anyway – by the statistics, that the last great hope for increasing road safety lay in the steady increase in women drivers. My reasoning was simplicity itself: that traditionally women were, and indeed still are, far less emotionally attached to cars and driving than men. Most women regard the car almost entirely in practical terms as a means of getting around, rather than as an aspect or extension of their personality. We saw this in Britain in the 1970s and early 1980s with the rise in the sale of the then generally uninspired Japanese cars: they appealed to the increasing number of women car owners because they were so reliable, virtually the only quality they required. My only caveat was that driving was *too* unimportant for women, so they didn't concentrate enough on it.

Now I am not so sure that the differences between men and women on the roads are as great as I had thought, and am more convinced that the gap in attitudes is, regrettably, narrowing. Some of the evidence I looked at comes from a survey conducted by the British Automobile Association, which found that, when it comes to cars and contrary to perceived notions, there are probably few major differences between men and women. The priorities attached to the cars' qualities seemed much the same, although women rated security rather lower and injury prevention rather higher than men.

There is, however, one physiological point that I had not appreciated. Dr Pat Waller explains that 'On the whole, men appear to have better spatial ability than women. Obviously spatial ability is very important in manoeuvring a car down the highway, when you're trying to park a car in a tight space. There's certainly overlap between the two sexes but, even outside of driving, I think it's fairly consistently found that men do better on that kind of spatial intelligence than women, and women do better with verbal skills than men. However, when it comes to driving, a certain level of skill is essential – but it's not simply a matter of skill and, in fact, if you look at the people who do best on other performance measures they have worse driving records.'

History, and the contrast between different countries' attitudes towards women in general, explains a lot. 'When driving started, almost a century ago now,' says Steve Stradling, 'it was almost wholly a male preserve and for a long time driving has been viewed as a male activity. In the UK at the moment about 80 per cent of eligible males are licensed to drive but only about 50 per cent of eligible females, but that means that among the males that figure has now plateaued and is not likely to increase much, whereas the proportion of eligible females who are driving is still climbing and is likely to go on climbing. So the proportion of female drivers on the road is going to continue to increase.

'There's an interesting difference between northern and southern Europe on this. The proportion of eligible females that drive is much higher in northern Europe and is still very low in southern Europe, where it is still largely a male activity that some women do, whereas in northern Europe it's becoming more and more a unisex activity and this has consequences for male drivers who are finding, as it were, the make-up of the road changing year by year, and they are having to accommodate continually to increasing proportions of female drivers.

'I guess other drivers are mostly just like me, and that I can predict what other drivers are likely to do by assuming that everybody else will do what I'd do in that situation. As the proportion of female drivers increases men are likely to be more and more out of kilter.

'There are more accidents involving male drivers than there are accidents involving female drivers, but there are a number of reasons for this. Firstly, there are still more male drivers on the road so, by chance alone, more accidents are going to involve men. Secondly, male drivers drive higher mileages than female drivers: in the UK the average male driver does about 18,000 kilometres a year and the average female driver about 11,000, so male drivers are likely to be more exposed to the risk. The third important point, and the insurance companies have known this for a long time which is why they offer lower premiums to women drivers, is that when they do have crashes, women drivers are more likely to have low damage, not fatal shunts, and when male drivers have crashes they are more likely to have big, explosive, high-speed, high-impact, damaging, fatal collisions.'

Dr Waller adds that 'If you look at low-mileage women compared with low-mileage men or high-mileage women compared with high-mileage men, the women do at least as well as the men and possibly a little better.'

The attitude differences are real enough. Steve Stradling distinguishes between 'skill at the wheel and safety-mindedness at the wheel. Typically, male drivers are better at skill, but women drivers are more safety-minded, so men drivers are better at doing hand-brake turns, believing they can stop on a sixpence, believing they can handle the beast at speed because they understand how engines work, and what the forces involved are in going round corners and they like more thrills. By contrast, female drivers are more likely to empathize with other drivers and to see the consequences of their actions if they drive badly and to anticipate what the consequences of their actions will be for other drivers. There's the big distinction between males and females, whether in the car or out, which is that males tend to be more competitive and comparative, whereas females tend to be more co-operative and that makes a difference.'

As Leonard Evans of General Motors points out, 'In general males are more likely to die violent deaths from every cause you can think of, including suicide, drowning, freezing to death, and it's the same pattern in traffic. Young males are the major core of the problem, both in terms of deaths to themselves and deaths to others when they're involved in crashes. There seem to be intrinsic differences between the sexes when it comes to behaviours that have a risk or activity factor. If we look at the number of pedestrian deaths to males compared to the number of pedestrian deaths to females, we find that every year the male rate far exceeds the female rate. This invites an interpretation that this may have something to do with testosterone, that males are doing things in traffic that relate to maleness in a very basic way.'

Steve Stradling adds that 'Men and women take risks differently. Most men enjoy the feeling of daring or the feeling of danger that risk-taking provides and, in fact, if you take a risk and get away with it there's a certain excitement, a certain gratification.'

'In our society,' says the American psychologist Larry Zeitlin, 'men find it very difficult to get a feeling of macho manhood, if you will. Society is very sanitized and men like to take risks simply because society doesn't provide many opportunities to exercise manhood, to exercise the bravery that our culture tends to demand of men. Taking risks is a way of proving yourself to yourself, so young men in particular take risks and they usually get away with them. Driving fast is one of those risks, disobeying traffic regulations is another. Women are much more reluctant to take risks because society doesn't demand that most women prove their bravery. That may change, these days, but so far risk-taking is mostly on the side of men.'

Hence the distinction made by Conrad King between the types of accidents which men and women have: 'Men are more likely to have accidents as a result of risk-taking, driving too fast. Women are more likely to have an accident at lower speed and through not concentrating on what another road-user's doing. Now, the way things are changing is that as women have been treated much more as equals in society, they're becoming much more aggressive as drivers. Any physical imbalance in terms of strength is now irrelevant because they're behind the wheel of powerful cars. Increasingly women drivers are driving more aggressively, faster. Paradoxically, insurance companies like women drivers: it's cheaper to insure a big, powerful sports car for a woman than it is for a man, which means they get to drive faster cars, they get to drive more powerful, more luxurious cars and they pay less for it, and as a driving group they're beginning to drive more and more like men. I'm not sure whether that's a good thing or not but it means that we're having more aggressive women on the roads as well as a bunch of generally quite aggressive men, which means a lot more aggressive people driving.'

The times, roles and role models sure are a-changing with the new breed of women described by Conrad King. And that, according to Steve Stradling, could also be men's fault. 'As women are taking over more men's roles out of the car,' he says, 'maybe what they're doing on the road is driving more like men. From a safety point of view this is probably bad news. Typically female drivers are more deferential and male drivers are more aggressive and demanding on the roads but that is beginning to change.'

Another group which is growing in importance is the increasing number of people of retirement age and over who drive. As Steve Stradling observes: 'Twenty years ago a very small proportion of those who reached retirement age held full driving licences. So the demographics of the road is in an interesting state of flux at the moment, which is going to add additional demands to all drivers.'

The prognosis is not good, partly, as Pat Waller says, because those involved have not adjusted to the results of these demographic changes. 'If you look at vehicle design and you look at highway design, or even driver-licensing procedures for that matter, none of these systems ever took into account the older user, and yet it's assumed that this older person, both as a driver and as a pedestrian, can do things that we have pretty good evidence that they can't. I don't think there's any question that older drivers have more difficulty with the system than other drivers,' he says firmly.

'We find crash rates per mile are very high for the young beginner driver. Then the crash risk per mile driven begins to rise again in the late fifties and rises at an accelerating rate thereafter so that by the time somebody is up in their late seventies or eighties the crash risk per mile is, if anything, higher than it is for the teenage driver. Older drivers are able to do as well as they do for as long as they do because they have the benefit of so much experience and judgement. Certainly some of the faculties that are necessary for safe driving begin to fail long before we reach our fifties. Most of us note major vision changes starting at least in the forties but I think the additional experience and the judgement that comes with that enable us to compensate for our failing faculties in other areas. But by the time people are getting up to their late fifties, we begin to see deficits occurring in the overall driving performance.'

If the oldies are a surprisingly bad risk, then so, far less surprisingly, are the young in whom, as Waller says, the problems are mostly inexperience and some deliberate risk-taking. Statistically, by far the riskiest driver on the road is one aged between nineteen and twenty-four, driving an old but powerful car late at night in a 40–50 m.p.h. zone. To make matters worse, young drivers apparently have slower reaction times and a poorer perception of the risks involved to themselves as well as to others.

'Their problem,' says Waller, 'is, of course, primarily inexperience, and that some engage in deliberate risk-taking. Much of what we call risk-taking behaviour in young drivers is not necessarily perceived as risk by a young driver: they simply don't recognize the risk. Research conducted in the United Kingdom shows that a beginning driver in their twenties will not be as bad as a beginning driver in their teens, but the biggest difference comes from the experience, not the age.' The experts may also underestimate the exhibitionist factor, that young drivers like to show off their new-found skills and their newly bought cars. One early study by Stradling's Manchester group found that almost every type of driver drove faster when they were alone, except young male drivers who drove faster when they had young male passengers.

If showing off to your peer group is an inevitable component of the adolescent male mentality, so is the desire to prove yourself. Siamack Salari, of J. Walter Thompson, notes: 'I remember when I was a student driving a Citroën 2CV. I'd drive it like a lunatic, aggressively, whereas when I used to drive my dad's big Citroën Prestige I'd be completely calm because it was a nice big car and I didn't have to prove anything to anyone.'

But in the end, says Bob Gunther, the way we drive is a reflection of our attitudes and personality, and the latter, at least, is almost impossible to change: 'I believe people drive the way they live. The way most of us live is as if we're immortal. We all have a basic awareness that some day we're going to die but we keep it out of our minds – to have that in our awareness would be too burdensome, we wouldn't be able to get anything accomplished, but it's always just under the surface. I believe we drive the same way: we have some basic fundamental awareness that at any moment we could be in an automobile crash and this tool that we're inside of could be turned against us, but we keep that awareness under the surface so that we don't have to deal with the weight of it, and we drive as if we could never crash.'

9

A Question of Risk

People are disposed to take more risks on the road than in the war, because usually they have a feeling that they control the situation and nothing bad will occur to them, unfortunately when it occurs the first time, very frequently it is the last time too.'

Jose Miguel Trigoso, head of the official
Portuguese road safety organization

As we saw in the last chapter, drivers tend to underestimate the degree of risk involved, which leads to a series of questions about the way we perceive risks and to what extent we are prepared to accept them. Honest experts, like David Silcock, an experienced traffic engineer, admit that 'the road-safety community has a very poor understanding of how drivers perceive risk. Research is going on into hazard perception, the way in which drivers perceive the different road features, and we're beginning to understand the interactions but it varies from individual to individual – from the time of day to whether you're in a hurry, whether you had a good night's sleep. These things are difficult to understand and to quantify.'

Larry Zeitlin, the psychologist, says: 'Risk isn't all the same. If you feel that you can control the danger when you are driving a car, you're much more willing to risk yourself than if you feel that you can't control the danger. We will accept a much higher rate of accidents in automobile driving, for example, than we will as passengers in aircraft. Also, if you get something from taking a risk – if you're in what's called a participative risk situation – you're willing to risk a lot more. If something is imposed on you from outside, of course, you demand the utmost safety. Probably the best example I can give is if someone puts you on top of a mountain and straps some boards to your feet and says, "I'm going to push you down the hill." Would you do it? You'd probably run screaming for help but yet there are millions of people who voluntarily go skiing every year.'

'We willingly take these risks,' says Professor Gerald Wilde of Queens University, Ontario, 'just as we're willing to take other risks, in hopes of achieving something. The art of life – and the art of driving – is not to minimize risk because it would mean we would stay at home and refuse to participate in all road use. No, the art of life, of meeting the challenge that is posed by risk, is to take the precise amount of risk, no more, no less, that is necessary to maximize the benefits from the activity in question, as in driving, for instance.'

Professor John Adams, of University College, London, feels that 'Everyone has in their heads a risk thermostat. Some have them set very high – the Hell's Angel, racing-car driver perhaps – others have them set very low, like the archetypal timid and cautious little old lady, but I've yet to meet anyone who's persuaded me that they've got a zero setting. The idea of a life without risk I personally find inconceivable. Even if it were possible I don't believe it would be desirable. It would just be unutterably boring. So we all take risks, and if we take risks, by definition there will be accidents.

'It's from having accidents and surviving them and learning from the experience, or reading about them in the newspapers, seeing them on television, being warned about them by our parents, that we acquire our perception of what is safe or dangerous. Then, if the balance between the danger level we perceive and the danger level that we're content with gets out of balance, I believe we behave in a way that reasserts the level of balance that we were originally content with. So, for example, if you fit a car with better brakes and there's no adjustment to the setting of the risk thermostat, people drive faster, start braking later, and the potential safety benefit is consumed as a performance benefit. Now that leads into speculation about how the risk thermostat is set. There are not only adverse consequences associated with taking risks, there are also rewards. What determines the setting?

'Well, if you're a motorist, it could be getting to the church on time, and it's, well, money, power, love, glory, sex, rushes of adrenaline, whatever turns you on. We have this complex mixture of motives for taking risks and that I see as the input that determines the setting of the thermostat.' For Adams 'the most interesting policy question that can be asked about the risks we take is who is imposing risk upon whom?'

This is possibly the fundamental question that can be asked about motoring and the dangers it involves: who should enjoy the power on the road? 'You have this mix of traffic,' says Adams. 'You have people in cars, juggernaut lorries, motorcycles, bicycles and people on foot, and on foot you have old people, adults, children. As traffic has built up there has been a progressive retreat on the part of vulnerable road-users. And if traffic continues to grow, the retreat almost inevitably will continue, and the question that I find interesting is, do we think this is fair?'

How is the risk thermostat in our heads regulated? 'Intuitively,' says Gerald Wilde. 'The measurement of risk is done on the basis of one's distance from other cars, the speed of other cars, the presence or absence of pedestrians, the quality of the road, the kind of car one is driving and so on. Other factors contribute to it, like road accidents that have happened to oneself or one's friends or relatives, or reading about road accidents or seeing them on television. It's known that when people pass a site on the road where an accident has happened they drive somewhat slower than they did before for the next five or ten minutes.

'The sense of protection you get from a vehicle will immediately influence the amount of risk you perceive. For instance, in a solid saloon car I would feel more relaxed because I know that if something happens I will probably not get injured very badly. But if I was driving around in a Morris Minor in London traffic, I think I would perceive an amount of risk much greater than I do now and I would adjust my behaviour accordingly.'

An interesting example of how people change their behaviour in the face of new conditions took place in Sweden. In the autumn of 1967 one Sunday morning at 4 a.m. the country changed from driving on the left to driving on the right. The government and its psychologists, engineers and statisticians predicted a major increase in the road-accident rate because drivers had not been able to prepare for the change: they obviously hadn't practised driving or being a pedestrian in right-hand traffic and it was thought that they would easily revert to old habits.

I was in Stockholm as a journalist for this supposedly Great Event. I remember vividly what a non-event it was, how the authorities held a press conference every hour late into the night and all they had to report was that some poor old lady up country had fallen off her bicycle. Indeed, my most striking memory of it was of the salt tang of the sea that permeated central Stockholm, which had been declared a traffic-free zone for the whole weekend. Clearly the Swedes, and not only their government, were being ultra-cautious.*

According to Gerald Wilde, 'A year later it turned out that the fatal accident rate per head of population had dropped by about 17 per cent, the opposite of what had been predicted. But a year and a half after that the figures had reverted to normal. So what happened? According to the people who analysed the behaviour of the Swedes, the changeover itself gave rise to a sudden increase in the amount of risk they perceived so that it was much

---

*I also remember a hilarious moment late in the evening when the then chairman of London Transport was asked up onto the podium. He'd clearly had a good dinner and when he was asked whether he thought the British would also go over to driving on the right of the road he replied simply, if not terribly clearly, that 'I've got enough bloody problems running London's transport system to think of that horror.'

higher than the risk they were willing to live with. They became very cautious and the accident rate dropped. But then the government became eager to let the population know that the problem had been contained, that there hadn't been a disaster, in fact the roads were safer than they had been before. People discovered for themselves that things were not as bad as had been predicted, and as they had expected, so the perceived level of risk went down again. They became less cautious and the accident rate went up. So there was an effect but it was short term, and ironically it was exactly the opposite of what the authorities had expected. If they had wanted a longer term effect, maybe as some jokers in the field have suggested, the government would have changed the traffic law again a year later, reverting back to traffic on the left and so on *ad infinitum* – but that, of course, also has its problems!'

The risk analysts are now prepared to contemplate the abolition of compulsory motor insurance. 'It's an odd topic,' says Professor Wilde, 'because at one point automobile insurance was forbidden in some countries – France, for example. It was felt that if people could buy themselves protection against the consequences of bad driving, they would allow themselves to drive badly. Now automobile insurance is mandatory, exactly the opposite. People feel protected against the accidents they have and the penalty for having an accident is much less than if you had to pay for the damage caused by an accident is much less than if you had to pay for the damage caused by an accident in which you were at fault.

'Some people in the field of accident prevention, accident causation, have tried to estimate what percentage of all accidents are due to automobile accident insurance. It is unquestioned that insurance has a major effect upon human behaviour: the fact that you can buy it will lead to behaviour change. Of course, the unfavourable effect of insurance upon accidents, that having insurance increases the likelihood of accidents, can be offset by insurance schemes that, for instance, give major discounts in premiums for accident-free driving. In one country, for instance, if you drive for ten years without an accident you get your insurance coverage for free. This is a strong motive for people to play it safe on the road. It is also known, from recent studies in Norway, that if people were promised a discount, or even a refund of the insurance premium they had paid, for being accident free, the accident rate reduced by something like 15 or 20 per cent.

'The insurance industry is in a position to control people's willingness to take risk but whether the companies will do this is another matter: they make money on the basis of the existence of a risk factor. If there were no accident risk, then people would not be willing to buy insurance against it. So accident reduction is not in the financial interest of the insurance industry.'

Reducing risk or perceived risk, or both, will encourage drivers to minimize it altogether and increase the accident rate. Psychologically we set ourselves the level of 'acceptable risk' and adjust our behaviour accordingly: if we feel comfortable in a fast car, are confident of its capacity to brake or accelerate when faced with potential danger, we find acceptable a higher level of risk. Researchers find that when drivers test new equipment, such as anti-skid brakes, they emerge from the car with remarks like 'getting away with murder'. 'We all operate on a given level of risk,' says Gerald Wilde. 'If you have safety devices in the car that lower the risk, your driving becomes more dangerous to compensate for the added safety. One American expert, E. Scott Geller, compares the phenomenon with that of American football players: the greater the protection they enjoy the greater the physical risks they are prepared to accept.'

Perhaps most obviously, 'risk compensation' enters the driving picture when it comes to weather. In general, drivers take account of bad conditions so accident rates don't necessarily increase in bad weather. But there are exceptions: when drivers have been warned of fog but set off in clear weather, typically they block out the warnings – and are not prepared for the risk when they hit a bank of fog. They can't adjust quickly enough to the changed conditions to avoid accidents.

As I was writing this book, I came across other such examples: the construction of a village bypass increased accidents in the village itself because people felt safer when they were driving through it. But despite all the circumstantial evidence that can be assembled to support a theory of risk compensation, it is hard to establish a statistical basis for it that will satisfy the scientists. As one researcher put it, 'Risk compensation is like the existence of God. You can't prove it.'

To my knowledge, the phenomenon was first observed in 1911 by Winston Churchill as home secretary when he told a trade union delegation that 'Few accidents arise . . . from ignorance of how to drive, and a much more frequent cause of disaster is undue proficiency leading to excessive adventure.' Even though his reply apparently aroused 'great laughter' he was right. Twenty-six years later a technical paper reported that: 'Better brakes do not necessarily lead to higher levels of safety.' This finds a contemporary echo in the curious case of the taxi firm in Munich, which recently got rid of all its cars with anti-lock brakes after its drivers' safety records went into a steep decline.

As Professor Gerald Wilde reflects: 'People manufacture and purchase cars with all kinds of new-fangled safety equipment, like air-bags, seat-belts, anti-lock brake systems, collapsible steering columns, and padded windshields. These cars look like immortality apparatus. It's very difficult to kill yourself protected by all this steel, plenty of space, wide tyres and so forth, but these vehicles, which are seen as safe, invite a change in driving style. In a car like this you will drive differently from the way you would drive an old T Ford.'

Even more dangerously, drivers who are, or think themselves, more skilful than the average are likely to be less so. For instance, it has been shown that drivers trained on a skid pan are more likely to have an accident in a skid than those who haven't. According to Gerald Wilde, 'A skid for the untrained driver is an unknown danger, to be scared of and avoided at all costs. But if you are familiar with skidding, perhaps even comfortable with it, you won't be so wary of it.

'Back in the early seventies there was a proposal at the national level [in the USA] for what was called a master-driver licence. The National Association of Race Car Drivers was pushing very hard for it. However, some researchers at the Insurance Institute for Highway Safety then looked at the road-driving records of these race-car drivers, taking into account their reported annual mileage and comparing them with other drivers of the same age. They found that race-car drivers had worse records than other drivers, and that's probably not surprising. The more skilful driver is likely to try things that maybe the rest of us wouldn't because we would think that maybe we're not up to handling that situation, and I think these kinds of compensations make up for any differences in high-level skill. There's no question that a certain minimum level of skill is essential if you're going to be able to manage on the highway at all, but beyond that it seems to be other factors that make a difference between the good driver and the not so good driver.'

The over-compensation for the increased safety drivers perceive in well-equipped cars provides excellent ammunition for freedom-obsessed campaigners, mostly in the United States. John Semmens* points out†, quite correctly, that with air-bags fitted only on the driver's side of the car, passengers were killed at a rate 50 per cent faster than in cars without any air-bags. He refers to serious studies that showed that seat-belts may help car occupants but lead to increased accidents to cyclists and pedestrians.

Indeed, the concept of risk compensation has caused a major question to be raised over seat-belts. John Adams, of University College, London, says, 'When the seat-belt law was introduced in Britain, it was claimed frequently in parliamentary debates that it would save a thousand lives a year. Well, no one is currently making that claim. The most recent version is two hundred lives a year, but I believe that is a huge exaggeration. I believe that there is no evidence that the law has saved any lives, not only in Britain but in any other country.'

In 1981, Adams conducted a study 'looking back at the countries that

*Formerly an economist for the Laissez Faire Institute, now a senior planner at the Arozona Department of Transportation, and a policy adviser to the Heartland Institute.
†In articles from the *Freeman* over the past few years, sponsored by the Advocates for Self-Government.

had passed seat-belt laws in the seventies. The study covered seventeen of the most motorized countries in the world, which contained about 80 per cent of the world's cars. Thirteen had passed seat-belt laws and four had not. The study suggested that the laws had had no effect. In fact, the countries that had not passed seat-belt laws enjoyed a slightly steeper decrease in fatalities than the countries that had. The next study that I know of was commissioned by the [British] Department of Transport, in which they looked at eight European countries. They concluded that the evidence did not support the Department of Transport's claim that a thousand lives a year would be saved [by the compulsory wearing of seat-belts]. They found no evidence of any saving of lives. Unfortunately that report was not permitted to inform the parliamentary debate about seat-belts. It was suppressed. I only learnt about it four years after it had been written and it was leaked to the *New Scientist* magazine.'

Adams's crucial point was that the laws were mostly passed in the mid-seventies, in the aftermath of the 1973 energy crisis: 'This seemed to be associated with a steep decline in the number of road accidents and road-accident fatalities. It didn't seem to matter whether you had passed a seat-belt law or a speed limit or both, or done neither. The results seemed to be the same. I think the most reasonable explanation for that is that throughout the world there was this pervasive publicity about the benefits of light-footed driving. Everyone was anxious about the world running out of oil and they were driving more slowly and carefully and perhaps more anxiously.

'In 1989 the study was repeated in the Department of Transport's eight countries by Wil Jansen in the Netherlands. He came to exactly the same conclusion, that there was no evidence of any saving of lives. In his 1991 book, Leonard Evans observed that by that time eighty jurisdictions throughout the world had passed seat-belt laws and, with one exception, in none of those countries can you see evidence for any beneficial effect of seat-belts in the accident outcome.

'His argument in favour of seat-belts was that they provide protection in a crash and that is not disputed. But that leads to a mystery: why do you have eighty jurisdictions all around the world passing laws requiring people to use seat-belts, which provide real protection in a crash, and yet you cannot see the result in the accident outcome? I believe the most plausible explanation is that risk compensation has been at work, that people driving with that slight extra sense of security are driving that slight bit more heedlessly.

'Britain is frequently cited in the literature as the one exception, the one country where you can see a clear response in the accident statistics to the passage of a seat-belt law. Now the law was passed in 1983. Also in 1983 the evidential breath-testing machine was introduced, which means that, for the first time, the evidence from a breath-testing machine could be used in court. You didn't need urine or blood tests to establish a case of drunken driving. In 1983 unprecedented numbers of breath tests were administered and there were unprecedented numbers of prosecutions for drinking and driving. There was a large decrease from 36 per cent to 31 per cent in the number of dead drivers who were over the legal limit and, perhaps most important of all, almost all the 23 per cent decrease in road deaths in that year was between the hours of ten at night and four in the morning – what are known in the trade as the drink-drive hours. In all the other hours of the day, there was no statistically significant decrease in road deaths. All the evidence therefore points powerfully to the reduction in road deaths in 1983 as being the result of the change in the drink-driving legislation. Yet it is claimed in all the official reports that it was caused by the seat-belt law. If you look closely at the figures for 1983, you discover that there appears also to have been a transfer of risk: the small decrease in the number of motorists killed was offset by an increase in the numbers of pedestrians, cyclists and people in the back seats of cars killed. This risk was transferred from motorists to other people who might be described as more vulnerable road-users.'

Unfortunately for Adams's theory, though, the trend line since 1984 has been downwards, the reduction in deaths being greater for pedestrians than for motorists. As so often, it is virtually impossible to distinguish between the effects of the two measures involved – the tightening of the laws against drink-driving and the compulsory wearing of seat-belts – but seat-belts undoubtedly played some, important part in the trend, which is not confined to the night-time hours when drink plays such an important role in crashes. My own belief is that Adams leaves out two important points: drivers' behaviour if they didn't have to belt up; and the undoubtedly enormous contribution made by belts to preventing injuries to car occupants in crashes. I strongly suspect – I know that it's true in my case – that were I not to wear a belt I would drive more carefully for a period of time, but then human nature would soon out and I would creep back to my old driving habits, a feeling reinforced by what happened in Sweden after they changed to driving on the right. And Adams does not dispute the overwhelming evidence that the use of a seat-belt improves a car occupant's chances of survival (an analysis cited by Adams is that it reduces death rates by 41 per cent).

But perhaps my most vivid reason for reacting against Adams's conclusions is emotional, not so much that Diana, Princess of Wales, might have survived if she had been wearing a seat-belt – the front-seat passenger, in a far more exposed position, was wearing one and survived – but the case recounted by the veteran Dr Howard Baderman. He remembers 'as a very typical accident [in the days before seat-belts] a young child who travelled in the front seat of her parents' car early one evening to go and buy something for supper. There was a collision – local street, low traffic speed and so forth – sufficient to throw her through the windscreen of that car. She was brought here, had instantly lost the sight of both eyes. The trauma for that child was huge and it would affect her for the whole of her life. It would also affect her parents for the whole of their lives too, and the tragedy for us was not simply that but we now know that that damage was totally avoidable, had seat-belts been available as they could have been and should have been.'

As cars grow ever safer, so, says Alison Smiley, 'does our confidence and the level at which we set our internal thermostat when driving. Not surprisingly, when we are not feeling optimistic the thermostat level falls, and so do road casualties during an economic depression.'

'I suppose,' says Daniel McCarthy, a road safety officer in Exeter, Devon, 'the corollary is if you want to make drivers drive more safely, that you should make them feel less safe.'

10

The Footsloggers

I can drive a car, I do occasionally drive a car, I choose not to drive a
car most of the time because I enjoy the excitement and danger of
being a pedestrian!
John Whitelegg, Professor of Environmental Studies, John Moores
University, Liverpool

'When roads were made,' said the Bishop of Ely in 1934, 'they were
intended to be pressed by feet as well as by wheels, and pedestrians had the
right to walk with comfort and assurance on the King's Highway.' Today,
though perhaps rather less than in the 1930s, pedestrians – the 'poor bloody
infantry' among road-users – remain the near forgotten element in the road-
safety equation. Statistically, says David Silcock, 'We've shifted the risk
from one section of the road community, those inside the vehicles, to
another section, those outside of the vehicles.' As we reduce the toll of
drivers and passengers, researchers have come to realize that, however safe
the cars for their passengers, they were still as dangerous to pedestrians, who
account for two in every five deaths on the road. Four times as many
children are killed or seriously injured as pedestrians than as car occupants.
In pedestrian casualties, Britain fares badly – a notable contrast to its lead
in overall road-safety figures – with more deaths relative to its population
than the Netherlands or the Scandinavian countries.

Michael Montague describes the situation, in a foreword to the official
pamphlet *What's Wrong with Walking*, as 'a walking disaster'. Perhaps, he
goes on, 'It is because walking is so commonplace that it is neglected –
pedestrians are so universal as to be almost invisible.'

'Whenever there is conflict between the needs of different road-users,
pedestrian interests tend to come last,' John Whitelegg says bluntly.
Everyone concerned with the roads, he adds, 'proceeds on the assumption
that priority should be given to drivers, not to other vulnerable road-users'.

When I read the figures for pedestrian deaths I was reminded of a film made twenty years ago, *Death Race 2000*, in which an evil American president diverted the public with a transcontinental race in which the winner was the driver who had killed most pedestrians *en route*. One of the most vivid images in the film was of a long line of wheelchairs containing elderly people lined up at the side of a road ready to be mown down.

Even though most of us are both pedestrians *and* drivers, to Whitelegg, 'These two animals are incredibly different in the way that they behave and in the way that they perceive things. The driver has no way of relating his or her pedestrian existence to his or her driving behaviour. The driver never says, "Oh dear, there's a pedestrian, I must take extra care because I am a pedestrian sometimes." The pedestrian behaves cautiously because he or she is frightened, and the driver and the pedestrian don't relate their relative experiences to the other side of the coin.'

Daniel McCarthy puts the pedestrian's situation in perspective: 'Drivers generally react according to the level of threat that they feel other vehicles represent to them, so car drivers generally will respond quite defensively when they're around large vehicles, buses and trucks, large vans, that sort of thing. The corollary is they will generally behave with less regard to the safety of vulnerable road-users, motorcyclists, pedal-cyclists and pedestrians, because these vehicles represent no real threat to the safety of the driver. Unfortunately the fact that drivers can then cause considerable harm to those vulnerable road-users is largely ignored.

'If you look at the way cyclists behave when confronted with the threat of cars, very often they will take to the pavements because that gets them out of the way of their predominant threat. But cyclists on pavements are generally viewed quite unfavourably by pedestrians who feel that they are under threat on what they might consider was their safe space.'

The result of this relative powerlessness, as Ben Plowden of the Pedestrians Association points out, is that 'the road network is functional, with every attempt being made to remove the obstacles in the drivers' path, while the pavements, the pedestrians' network, is dysfunctional, with no attempt being made to clear clutter, or to reduce the accidents that can befall the pedestrian by contact with inanimate objects [traffic-lights, etc.], let alone with the cyclists who so blithely use the pavement. Britain's Department of the Environment gave the game away when its booklet *The Common Inheritance* encouraged us to walk "where it is safe to do so".' The point about 'clutter' is particularly appropriate to Britain where pavements are blocked with unnecessary numbers of traffic-signals, which impede pedestrians and confuse drivers. The authorities in continental Europe contrive to place their far smaller number of traffic-lights on lamp-posts and other existing structures, while still providing better sight-lines for the driver.

The emphasis on the road-as-safe-for-drivers has resulted in a tendency to blame pedestrians for any accident in which they might be involved. For nearly seventy years, the Pedestrians Association has been insisting 'that it is very misleading to attribute the death of a pedestrian to his "becoming confused or hesitating" when the fatality would often be much more fairly and accurately attributed to the circumstances of the action which occasioned the hesitation, viz., (in most cases), excessive speed'.

Of course, efforts – mostly token ones – have been made to provide some relatively safe space on roads for pedestrians, with the introduction of pedestrian crossings; Belisha beacons were introduced in 1934 and zebra crossings twenty years later. World-wide studies of the effects of such crossings have shown them to be relatively ineffective. 'Unfortunately,' says Professor Gerald Wilde, 'after the installation of pedestrian crossings, with or without lights or with or without lines painted on the surface like the zebra stripes and so on, in some cases there has even been an increase in the number of pedestrians being injured or killed, due to the fact that these apparently safe facilities give pedestrians a false sense of security. As a result they pay less attention to approaching traffic and are more involved in accidents than they were before.'

For pedestrians the situation is getting worse, even if fewer are being killed. There has, says John Adams, 'been a huge shift in road-user rights and priorities. The reason that there are now far fewer pedestrians, children and cyclists killed in road accidents than there were decades ago is that they are deferring to the traffic. You don't find road-safety experts in schools teaching children their rights as road-users. The training is overwhelmingly devoted to inculcating deference to the car – and then some of them grow up and become transport planners and the cycle repeats itself.'

As Dr Bob Davis, chairman of the Road Danger Reduction Forum, puts it: 'Whatever the responsibilities of people walking or cycling, and however much we will always fail to walk and cycle in the proper way at all times, we should be emphasizing the responsibility of those people from where the danger originally comes. We should be concentrating on telling adults that they must drive properly, that it is unacceptable socially to do otherwise and not have to concentrate so much on telling our children to get out of their way.'

In his 1995 book, *Risk*, John Adams notes that 'In 1971 80 per cent of seven- and eight-year-old children in England travelled to school on their own, unaccompanied by an adult. By 1990 this figure had dropped to 9 per cent; the questionnaire survey disclosed that the parents' main reason for not allowing their children to travel independently was fear of traffic.'

Many children have been removed from danger by their parents, but the elderly are even more helpless because they are less mobile and their senses are less sharp. In Britain, as also, I suspect, in most European countries, they are also much more heavily dependent on their own two feet than the younger generation. Far fewer have cars (four out of five of the under-sixties have a car in their household, a figure which drops to under a quarter for eighty-year-olds). The resulting dependence and vulnerability means that 9000 pedestrian pensioners are killed or injured every year. Pedestrians over sixty-five are 2.5 times as likely to be killed as those under retirement age, and the rates increase: males of over eighty-five are five times as likely to be killed as the sixty-five-year-olds. (The rates for women are markedly lower.)

It is easy enough to generalize about pedestrian habits, but, as David Silcock warns, 'it's complicated [to get at the truth] because we have limited information about the amount of travel by pedestrians and cyclists. Accidents can drop for two reasons: you can reduce the risk of an accident, or you can reduce the opportunity for it to happen. People may find crossing the road safer or they may choose not to cross the road at all. Either of those conditions will lead to fewer road accidents and we are very uncertain about the exposure side, the numbers of opportunities for crossing the road or walking along the sidewalk.'

For Adams there has been 'no real improvement in road safety in developed societies. There is a withdrawal of the elderly, the young, the people experiencing handicaps or problems, who avoid dangerous situations, with the result that fatalities and accidents go down. The situation itself is as dangerous as ever. If we look at normal behaviour in a town or a city, and we could examine the ways in which people moved around in 1950 and 1960, 1970, 1980, what we'd see is that over that period of time people have withdrawn: they walk to school less, they walk to shops less, they use a car for very short journeys, they don't make contact with their neighbours over short distances on foot or by bicycle. People have voluntarily abandoned the street and retreated into their vehicles for what they perceive to be safety. We've let the streets become colonized by cars and the result of this is that cars are dominant and pedestrian accidents go down.'

As we saw with seat-belts, what Adams is saying and writing is inherently unprovable, and he is in danger of over-romanticizing the past, when discussing the past and present situation of pedestrians. Cars have made large numbers of old people more mobile, more active than their forebears; while, historically, for every middle-class child walking or cycling peacefully to school, a dozen working-class children played in streets that were car-free because cars were beyond the economic reach of the inhabitants. They played there because no other open spaces were available.

Not surprisingly, the warfare between pedestrians and other, more powerful road-users is at its most intense, and its bloodiest, in a city like New York. Larry Zeitlin, a psychologist, points out that the Big Apple 'is typical of cities, where accidents are different from accidents in most other areas. Driving is so congested that the accidents are basically slow speed, fender-bender collisions. It's costly, it's inconvenient in time and money, insurance rates are astronomical but relatively few people get killed in automobile accidents.' Inevitably, those who do are pedestrians. 'They're at greatest danger in New York. The pedestrians and the automobiles are competing for very limited space, and particularly on right turns the pedestrians and automobiles try to share the same space at the same time and neither is willing to give way. If an automobile and a pedestrian tries to share the same space at the same time the pedestrian comes off the worst. The city is very crowded, with people and cars, and the densities of both and the time pressures on both are so great that few people are willing to obey all the rules and many put themselves at risk.'

For a description of the front line you can't do better than hear from a New York motorcycle courier, appropriately named Bandit: 'Pedestrians don't like it when we don't stop. They're always yelling at us that we should stop for the red light, cursing us, but we're just trying to make a living, and when you're on commission it's not easy, because some days are slow, then you get fast busy days. If it's a slow day you're going to hustle harder, if it's a busier day then you know you have time to slow it down a little bit because you know your bag is loaded up and you have a lot of work so you're OK. But they [pedestrians] don't like us, period. That's the bottom line. People won't get hurt as long as they cross the street like they're supposed to, but a lot of people break rules themselves. They jaywalk and when they jaywalk the traffic goes out of order and then, boom, they get hit.

'I hit a couple of people, and biking keeps you fit and strong so when I hit someone I know a way not to fall off the bike. I just keep going but the person will bounce a couple of feet away and they get hurt. I always stop and find out if they're OK, even when they're upset, cursing me, but once I see they're on their feet and they're walking then I just keep going.'

Steve, his controller, paints a vivid picture of Manhattan's version of Armageddon. 'It's really hard because in New York you have your pedestrians, you have bicycle riders and you have motor vehicles and nobody is obeying the law. Jaywalking in New York is a two-dollar fine and it's never enforced so people just cross the street where they like, and if they see car traffic is stopped they don't think that a bicycle's going to come zipping through so they just come out and that'll be that. A couple of winters ago an old lady fell down on the ice right in front of me and I'm riding in about two inches of snow and there was no way to turn. I just had to hit the ground so I don't run this lady over. Then I got harassed by the cops because I scared her.'

War equals aggression, from both sides. 'In my neighbourhood,' says Steve, 'they just had to put two speed bumps just to slow the cars down. So everybody in my neighbourhood comes out when they have nothing to do in the evening and they sit on the park benches and watch the cars set off sparks and cheer, because we're tired of cars ripping through the neighbourhood.' But he adds: 'Basically, if you're travelling in the city and if something happens to you, it's your own fault because you're not paying attention.'

Charlie Komannoff, a pedestrian activist, puts Bandit's and Steve's views into context: 'More pedestrians are killed in New York City than drivers in crashes and yet it's not talked about. It's not part of the political equation, it's not in the newspapers. Every year in America close to 6,000 pedestrians and 800 cyclists are killed on the roads, and yet no one in the road safety establishment, or the automobile corporations, or even in the public interest groups that represent consumers ever talks about pedestrian endangerment or pedestrian deaths. We don't even study pedestrian crashes well enough to understand how pedestrians are killed, why they are killed and how fewer pedestrians might be killed. If the same effort was put into pedestrian casualties that's put into driver and motorist casualties, maybe we could do something about the problem.

'To a great extent in New York City pedestrians and drivers are not the same people. Pedestrians are elderly, they are children, they are people too poor to have a car or people too green to use a car. So there's little consideration on the part of drivers for the pedestrians as people because they are seen as aliens instead of people like themselves.'

This does not stop the authorities from trying to blame pedestrians. According to Komannoff, 'A former transportation commissioner in New York City used to point out that a third of all pedestrian fatalities were drunk. It turned out he had misplaced the decimal point and a third of all pedestrian fatalities had one hundredth of one per cent alcohol in their bloodstream, which was only one-tenth of the legal limit, so maybe they had had a tiny bit to drink ten hours ago but they were legally nowhere near drunk. Yet this is part of the psychology of blaming the victim in pedestrian fatalities. It seems that every time a child is run over by a car it's said that he or she darted out into the car and the driver had no time to react. Well, if the driver had been going only 10 m.p.h. instead of 30 m.p.h. or if the driver knew that there would be terrible consequences for him if he ran into and injured a kid, then the drivers would exercise more restraint, and we wouldn't have car crashes being the number one cause of death among people in America under the age of fourteen.'

The problem in most major cities, including New York, which is a relatively pedestrianized city by American standards, is a simple question of priorities. Komannoff says: 'The traffic engineers have only one criterion and that is how fast they can get how many cars to move through the streets, and anything that impedes the flow of car traffic is something to be removed instead of something to be accommodated. If New York City were more like

Paris or Tokyo or even London, we would be accommodating the pedestrian, but we don't, and that's why pedestrian fatalities in New York are double those in Tokyo or Paris and 50 per cent more than that in London. You take a magnificently engineered machine, the motor-car, designed for speeds of 120 m.p.h. and you put it in a city where the legal limit is 30 m.p.h., where the standard speed is sometimes 10, 5 or even zero m.p.h., where bicyclists are whizzing past you, and you're going to make drivers frustrated. It only takes a few drivers being frustrated at a time to create a terrific climate of endangerment for the millions of people in New York who get around on foot. So it's no surprise that 250 pedestrians are killed in New York City every year. We are doing things wrong here as compared to what's happening in other world cities that are characterized by pedestrianism.'

Komannoff may compare New York unfavourably with other metropolises, but Londoners, Parisians and Berliners would all concur with his underlying theme: that private cars have no place in major cities. 'The car provides no real mobility in a crowded city like New York. It's a machine for creating frustration, for expressing anger, for expressing a macho attitude, and ultimately for running over and killing people.'

But while every country in the world has a car lobby or lobbies, the far greater number of pedestrians are barely represented. 'The pedestrian lobby in New York [or London or Paris] ought to be a powerful lobby. Most people get around a good part of their day by walking, most people take the subway or the bus and they walk to and from the subway or the bus station. New York is really a pedestrian-dominated city but it's not a pedestrian-oriented city and the interest groups that represent pedestrians are rather weak.

'America has painted itself into a corner as far as making killer drivers accountable because we've constructed a society where you pretty much need a car to get around. New York is the exception to that, not the rule, and juries or the public are loath to take away the driving privileges of people who've injured or killed pedestrians or other motorists because they know that it will ruin that person's life. On the other hand if motorists understood that their life might be ruined if they endangered or killed other people on the road, they might have a different attitude that would inform and change the way they drove. There have been studies showing that charges are less against drivers who run over and kill pedestrians than against drivers who kill other drivers.'

We're back here to the question of power. John Whitelegg agrees with John Adams that 'In a society that's already dominated to the extent it is in Europe and North America by cars, most people have very little choice about walking or cycling, because the environment is so dangerous. So people don't *choose* to go by car. People go by car because the alternatives are so dreadful. 'Cars are a bit like a vicious organism that has colonized our cities and exterminated all the alternatives. There's no alternative to the car.

'Road-safety measures are usually not well audited for the effect they actually have. A lot of road-safety measures are designed to channel people on to pelican crossings and zebra crossings or into underpasses underneath roads. In some way they try to restrict pedestrian access to roads. If you do things like that, you create a situation in which people do something to confound what you've tried to prevent them doing: people faced with an underpass won't use it, they'll run across the road, leap over a fence and into a dual carriageway. They might be killed. Now, whose fault is that? My view is that the traffic engineer who designed that road is responsible for that accident because pedestrians should not be forced underground.

'I think we can design cities in a way that will minimize if not eliminate the possibility of fatalities and serious road-traffic accidents. We can do that by making sure that vehicles go very slowly where they're likely to be in contact with people. We can eliminate vehicles from near schools, from near residential complexes, from near busy shopping centres. We can make arrangements so that huge areas of cities are, in fact, car free and we can do that sensibly and realistically by making sure that all the alternatives are in place to enable people to do what they've got to do.

'I think the design of cities has to include a fairly deep understanding of the psychology of driver behaviour and pedestrian behaviour. There's a joint responsibility here to do something about it but that still has to bear in mind the damage that a car driver can do at fifty miles per hour on an urban street by comparison to the damage that a pedestrian can do rushing around at four miles an hour.

'Having said that, the pedestrian's responsibility is to behave in a responsible way, just as it's the driver's responsibility to behave in a responsible way, and we can design an environment to encourage that amount of responsibility, to give pedestrians more road space. If you put them on a narrow footpath they're likely to wander off into the road, so widen the footpath. Give pedestrians easier ways of crossing streets: if you have to wait fifteen minutes at a pelican crossing for the green light to come on, you'll rush across in the middle of the traffic. If pedestrians can send the pelican crossing into green mode for pedestrians within a reasonable time, then the problem's solved, but our traffic engineers design pelican crossings to be nice to motorists and nasty to pedestrians, so we've got to start from that point.'

One gesture that motor manufacturers could make it an effort to reduce pedestrian injury would be to make the front of cars more pedestrian-friendly. The most dangerous vehicles are those with high ground clearance and ornaments, especially bull-bars – designed to show that the owner is used to herding cattle or elephants. These should be forbidden (or, at least, their owners assumed to be guilty if they ever hit a pedestrian). Some research has been done on this subject, notably at the Transport Research Laboratory which has what they call a Leg Firing Machine that tests the interreaction between the front of cars and parts of the human body. Perhaps it should be a permanent, compulsory exhibit in showrooms for vehicles fitted with bull-bars.

But even if we did smooth the front and rear of cars, the result would be a palliative, not a cure for an inherently unsatisfactory situation. 'We have a myth of the pedestrian-friendly bonnet,' says Daniel McCarthy bitterly. 'This makes you feel rather secure that if you were unfortunate enough to strike a pedestrian, your pedestrian-friendly front end would care for them and, sure, it's made a huge difference. But isn't it part of our dual thinking that we can even *talk* about a pedestrian-friendly bonnet? That if you're scooped off your feet at 30 m.p.h. the expanse of metal would caress you before it deposited you gently back on the tarmac?'

11

The Limits of the Law

In a democratic country, the government cannot go further in
enforcing safety regulations than public opinion is prepared to
support. We believe that inspection of vehicles would make for a
reduction in the number of road accidents, but if public opinion is not
prepared to put up with the added interference and inconvenience it
is clearly unwise for us to try to legislate ahead of public opinion.
Parliamentary secretary, Ministry of Transport, 1954

There is nothing more damaging to the legal system than attempts to
prevent behaviour that is both common and acceptable to a substantial
section of the public. As Prohibition showed in the USA seventy years ago
– and as the war against 'soft' drugs has been demonstrating with ever-
increasing clarity since the 1960s – there has to be some trade-off between
the public will and the law. If the two are out of synch then unpopular laws
irregularly and thus unfairly applied result, which leads to an increasingly
generalized lack of respect for the legal system as a whole. Ever since
governments tried to impose some discipline on the roads they have come
up against the unwillingness of motorists – still the most affluent, articulate
and influential section of the population – to conform. Crucially, some of
the laws involved – especially those regarding speeding – are so habitually
disregarded in many countries that enforcement presents insurmountable
difficulties in policing.

In speeding, the perceptions of speed and the capacities of cars have
changed enormously since speed limits were established, thirty years ago in
Britain. Today, cars are much faster and, more relevantly, their braking and
handling have improved immeasurably so that it takes less time for a family
saloon to come to a complete stop from 80 m.p.h. than it did to stop from
60 m.p.h. when the 70 m.p.h. limit was established. Road-safety
campaigners see the effects of high speed in terms only of the increased risk

and severity of accidents. But surely a new balance should be struck to bring the majority of drivers on motorways within the law. Far more would obey an 80 m.p.h. limit than the present 70 m.p.h. top speed. I know I would.

As it is, police seem rarely to stop a driver doing less than 80 m.p.h. and, as Larry Zeitlin says, 'People basically take risks because they get away with it. People don't obey the traffic rules because 99 per cent of the time nothing happens. They learn that rules are to be disregarded because if you disregard the rules you gain in time and convenience. The hundredth time, of course, something happens but that happens to an individual so infrequently that there's a learnt desire to ignore the rules.'

If restrictions are to be both acceptable and effective, which in many cases is the same thing, they have to be in line with the nature of the society involved: in Scandinavia drivers were already so aware of the dangers of drink that they barely needed drink-driving laws. In other countries the authorities have been able to harness the general revulsion against drunkenness – and against the consequences of driving while under the influence of drink – to ensure that the increasingly strict laws brought in over the past thirty years against drunken driving in most industrialized countries were both acceptable and enforceable.

Quite the opposite is the case with speeding, where a substantial proportion of drivers prefer to judge for themselves what speed is safe under any given conditions. Dr Pat Waller says: 'Throughout recorded history we know that value has been placed on the fastest runner, the fastest horse, the fastest ship, the fastest train, the fastest car, the fastest plane. This seems to be a characteristic of human nature that's simply been there for as long as we know anything about human beings. In that regard it would probably be more sensible to make cars that feel as if they're speeding at 70 or 80 m.p.h. when they're doing only 40 m.p.h. Instead we do just the opposite. We make cars that feel as if they're practically standing still when they're doing 70 or 80 m.p.h. We seem as a species to crave high speed but the problem is that we're not built to withstand the sudden stop when anything happens and so that's where we get into trouble.'

Perhaps the single most important problem is that we underestimate the time and distance necessary to stop a car at a given speed. Mike Doyle makes the points strongly. 'A safe stopping distance is far more than people realize. For instance, at 30 m.p.h., just a rough mental calculation of a stopping distance with a one-second reaction time is around 25 metres. If we take it to 40 and 50 m.p.h., it doesn't just become 50, 60, 70 metres, it grows exponentially. In other words, 10 m.p.h. above a certain speed, that is from 30 to 40 m.p.h., doesn't just increase your skidding displacement by a set amount, and going another 10 m.p.h. faster doesn't increase it by another set amount. It's an exponential increase, so at 30 m.p.h. a skidded displacement – that is, the actual skid marks that are left on the road surface

– might only be 12 metres, but at 40 m.p.h. it could be 23, 24 metres. At 50 m.p.h. it could be up to 60 metres.

'Now when you're travelling at 70 m.p.h., if you give a reaction time of perhaps one second, that coupled with the actual distance to stop is somewhere around the length of the average soccer pitch and that's with a one-second reaction time and that's a considerable distance. At 70 m.p.h., you are travelling at approaching 30 metres per second so there's 30 metres gone. If you sneeze you've covered 60 metres, half the length of a football pitch, and if someone in front has done something unpredictable, it could be the last time you sneeze.'

Paradoxically, say some experts – and most lorry drivers and their employers – speed may be a good thing for the economy, or indeed society as a whole. If you lower the speed limit, says Professor Gerald Wilde, it would reduce the accident rate, which would be good for the individual citizen, 'but wouldn't actually be a benefit to the nation. Although speed engenders the risk of accident, it also has a major economic benefit for people. Suppose we force people to drive half the speed they do now, it would take twice as long to move people and goods from A to B. Therefore it would become much more expensive, the system would become less efficient, manufacturers would make less money, workers would make less income. And governments would collect fewer taxes. There would be less money available for education or for medical care and, everything considered, maybe the balance would be negative. In other words, the risk of accidents is an inevitable part of an activity that brings benefits and to sacrifice part of that activity for the purpose of improving safety may be not to the net benefit of society.'

This sort of argument is manna to freedom-lovers like Csaba Csere, of Car & Driver. 'We are told that speed kills. I think the correct hectoring would be that inappropriate speed kills. Speed that's too fast for conditions kills, and that's where the driver has to make his judgement. Obviously going 90 m.p.h. in a school zone is too fast and it's going to kill people, but travelling 75 or 80 m.p.h. on a road that's straight and empty is hardly dangerous. There's more to the speed than simply the speed of the impact that will result from a crash. American drivers like to get where they're going, that's what transportation is about. Getting there sooner is better than getting there later. Getting there sooner also means you have a shorter travel time, you're less likely to be fatigued, you're going to be more attentive to your driving, so if you're driving on a road that is in very good condition, that is not full of cars, where you can see far ahead, I think you can drive a little bit faster than the posted speed limits.

'We've just seen evidence of this in the United States, because at the end of 1995 the Congress gave control of speed limits back to the individual states. Congress had taken away control of speed limits back in 1973–74 during the first energy crisis and it finally came back. The states responded quickly by raising speed limits. In Michigan we went up to 70 m.p.h. on most interstate highways, some other states went higher. Montana has no speed limit during the day right now, which is where Montana was in the old days. The safety advocates were insisting that there were was going to be a bloodbath on the highways, that traffic deaths would rise by 6400 was the common number. In fact, traffic deaths were basically unchanged between '96 and '95, the last year with the low speed limit. I think it's very hard to make the case that speed kills.' The argument is fiercely contested by the safety lobby, and the statistics seem to me inconclusive.

'I think speed should be largely up to the individual', says Csaba Csere, 'because it promotes the idea of driving responsibility. Most accidents in the US are caused by driver error and the only way you can prevent that is by making drivers be more attentive, responsible for their own actions. Forcing drivers to select their own speed is one of many areas of responsibility that we need to encourage because that's where the ultimate safety comes from.'

Charles Terlizzi, of the National Motorists' Association, claims that government studies show 'that the vast majority of our speed limits are posted too low. Typically they are set politically rather than according to engineering standards.' He says that the speed limit 'should be set at the speed at which people travel'. He also argues, however, that 'The vast majority of drivers on the road do know best what is the safest speed for the conditions, and that's the speed at which people will travel. If the speed limit does not represent that, then it's wrong for people to be charged and have their property and their rights taken away from them because they're disobeying a law that they cannot practically obey.'

He also emphasizes that 'the best speed for the road is the prevailing speed of traffic, the speed at or below which about 85 to 90 per cent of the traffic is travelling. The safest speed to travel is within 5 to 10 m.p.h. above or below that, so where the speed limit is 55 m.p.h., if everyone on this road is going 70 m.p.h., the police will set up a speed trap and they'll select the car out of the group that is going maybe 5 or 6 m.p.h. above that. The fact is that the person who is driving within 5 to 10 m.p.h. of that prevailing speed is doing nothing wrong. The law therefore is unreasonable.' It is impossible for the police to act effectively against the general will of the motoring population when it is expressed as a will to travel at a given speed.

As it is, the present situation encourages activists like Terlizzi to argue 'that traffic enforcement is more for revenue and politics than for safety. That's made obvious in that whenever they mount any kind of an enforcement campaign for any kind of a problem, they enforce speed limits because it's the easiest thing to catch a lot of people violating. And the speed limits are impractical, unworkable. The police know that if they want to stop a car for something else, chances are very good that that car's going to be exceeding an unrealistic speed limit, so they can stop the driver for that. They can use speed as a reason to harass motorists for other things.'

In the United States the conviction that all motorists have the right to speed is by no means universal. It is far more general in Germany. Mike Nowka is a typical German speed freak. To him, 'A high-performance car in the proper hands is not a dangerous toy. The people buying these cars mostly know what they are dealing with and what car they are driving. So I think the driver of the high-performance car is not the problem, the other drivers are the problem. People on an average road do between 100 to 120, 60 to 100, 70 k.p.h. and I always have the feeling that they are asleep because this kind of speed is not holding their attention on the road. They are playing with their mobile phones, they are playing with their radios. If you drive a real high-performance car you are fully concentrated on what you're doing.' To Nowka, speed 'is some sort of a thrill –some people do bungee-jumping, fly fighter planes. You enjoy the car, you enjoy the road and you enjoy driving, and from time to time you can go fast.'

And the fastest he ever drove on a public road? An unbelievable 380 k.p.h. (over 220 m.p.h.) in a McLaren F-1. 'But,' he adds, 'you can do this only under perfect conditions, weather wise and traffic wise, because it's very dangerous to drive with a very fast car on a public road and you should be aware of this.'

Nowka's attitude is not exceptional, but it is probably more honest than the majority of his compatriots. As Stradling says, 'In Germany, speed has become not only a transport issue but an issue about the freedom of the citizen. In Germany there's been a campaign for a number of years which is basically arguing that the lack of the speed limits on motorways is a fundamental right of the free citizen, free speed for free citizens, unlimited speeds for free citizens and the majority of German motorways are still without a speed limit. Traditionally in Germany the fatality record on motorways was astronomic, much higher than in any British motorway context, and for that reason the Germans invented in the mid-seventies a helicopter rescue system, to lift the nearly dead bodies away from the motorways and take them to a quick-repair station, a local hospital, to try to reduce the road-traffic accident fatality rate on motorways. That actually worked and reduced road-traffic accidents. Britain's very different from Germany in that we don't have any association between free citizens and unlimited speed. Brits accept speed limits far more than the traditionally law-abiding Germans, but we don't obey them. Every day we exceed the speed limit in our cities and we think it's fun, we're not bothered.'

The German opposition to limits is real enough, as Bernhard Potter found to his cost. In the late 1980s, he says, when the city government of Berlin included Green Party representatives, it tried to impose a speed limit of 100 k.p.h. on the autobahns. It was stopped by mass demonstrations organized by the German Automobile Club (ADC). In Germany not only is the motor industry itself enormously important, a symbol of the country's post-war success, but the ADC is immensely powerful. Almost every driver in Germany is a member, with a million in West Berlin alone. In the 1980s the freedom to drive at any speed you chose became a symbol – above all in Berlin – of more general freedoms enjoyed by West Germans.

As Potter explains, the ADC 'took up this fear of not being able to drive somewhere. They said East Germany is the only place where you have had a speed limit in German history, so they said speed limits means socialism, means you are being trapped behind a wall and you don't want that, so if you have West German values, democratic values, you have to be against the speed limit, which is totally crazy in my eyes, but it worked.' Even Potter has to admit that 'some of that is really true because what the East Germans lacked and missed most was mobility. They wanted to move, they wanted to drive their car.'

Over the past few years this automatic association of freedom to drive fast with freedom in general has had disastrous consequences. As Potter says: 'When East Germany joined West Germany, when it became one Germany again, the speed limit in East Germany was abolished. The East Germans wanted to get rid of their old cars which were much slower and also because they looked like they were from East Germany and everybody wanted to have something from West Germany. So a lot of people from East Germany went and bought new Western cars. Now these cars were high-powered cars – even if they only bought Opel they were twice, three times as fast as their old cars, and you could see a terrible rise in accidents.'

Bernhard Potter is talking only of Germany, but he summarizes a hypocritical attitude which is by no means confined to his own country when he says: 'If you have an opinion poll, should there be a speed limit and if you give people all the reasons, the wounded, the dead, the costs, the ecological reasons, they say, "Maybe it would be a good idea to have a speed limit on the autobahns – but not on the autobahns I'm driving on." And if you take an opinion poll on should there be a speed limit of 30 k.p.h. in the city, they would say, "Definitely, in the streets where I live and where my children live, so that they should be safe, but not on those streets I drive every morning to go to work." The funny thing is that when German drivers go abroad, to Italy, France, Spain, they obey the speed limit more or less, but as soon as they get into Germany again it's ridiculous to them to think of a speed limit.'

The result is that the Germans accept the consequences of their actions: they thought it natural to build a hospital virtually on a motorway intersection near Augsburg, far bigger than the city needed, largely to cope with victims of crashes on the autobahn.

The concept of driving as an inalienable right dogs the whole question of regulation enforcement and, as might be expected, finds its most extreme expression in people like Charles Terlizzi in the United States. 'The car is the tool of most of our basic freedoms in this country,' he says flatly. 'It's the vehicle that allows us to choose where we live, where we work, where we go to church, what we do for entertainment. It's been argued that we don't have a constitutionally guaranteed right to drive a car, that driving is a privilege. The problem I have with that is that if you deny what I consider the right to drive a car, you deny all of those other freedoms that are protected. If they declare driving a privilege, they will then declare all of the other rights and protections that we expect in every other aspect of our lives a privilege. Where driving is concerned people in this country tend to stand for government intrusion in our lives that we would not stand for under any other circumstances. By definition, a privilege is a perk that is granted on the whim of the grantor, in this case the governor of the state. If driving is in fact a privilege, then the governor could say today, "Well, we're not going to let any Democrats drive this year," so I have a problem with their declaring that someone has the authority in this country to issue privileges to select groups.' And Csaba Csere says simply: 'We really don't want Big Brother looking over our shoulders while we're driving because in America we don't want Big Brother keeping track of our every move in any aspect of our lives.'

In Terlizzi's eyes – and he's by no means alone – the concept of freedom extends also to the compulsory installation of air-bags and the wearing of seat-belts. 'The analogy has been drawn that if the government perceived an epidemic of some kind or a disease that needed to be cured, that we would certainly expect them to do something about it. Well, I think what we would expect them to do is to educate us, tell us what the risks are, but we wouldn't expect them to force us to take the cure.' For him, air-bags are 'a government programme that was supposed to have saved lives. They made these outrageous claims that they're going to save fifteen thousand lives a year when, in fact, in eleven years they've saved at best fifteen hundred and what that means is that every life saved, or every twenty-five lives saved, has cost us one. Now the government is implying that that's acceptable.' Even when he wears a seat-belt, 'typically when out on a long trip, I wear it not so much for the safety considerations but because it keeps me in a better position to control the car. I think, considering the fact that seat-belts have the potential to do harm, that it should be my choice, that I should be allowed to assess the risk versus the benefit of them and make a choice for myself as to whether or how I'm going to protect myself from the risks that I determine. I think it's not the place of the government to force remedies for perceived problems upon people. We're all adults.'

Again he's not alone. Csaba Csere believes that 'A seat-belt is absolutely the best safety device in an automobile and I think you are being irresponsible if you don't wear it all the time.' Yet, he says, 'I myself don't believe they ought to be compulsory. I think that there's room for individual freedom in seat-belt use, as there is in many other aspects of life, and I don't think the state should be telling people to wear their seat-belts.'

The installation of modern, generally electronic methods of preventing people from breaking the law – most obviously when speeding or driving across a red light – arouses even more widespread resentment. They also create their own problems of enforcement: many police forces in Britain admit that they do not have the resources to monitor the results of the electronically timed radar speed-measuring devices they have installed on many major roads. Steve Waller points out that 'The public, at least in the United States, seems to feel that that kind of automated enforcement is somehow unfair, that it's not giving the driver a fair chance to outsmart the enforcement. My own personal opinion is that if there's clear signing and clear warning to everyone involved that this is what's going on, then there is nothing wrong with it. It's certainly a much safer approach to enforcement than trying to pull people over to the side of the road where there's a lot of traffic going at high speeds or on bridges or places where it's just hazardous. You can create a greater hazard by stopping a speeding driver than by just ignoring it and letting them go.'

Curiously, Csaba Csere is in favour of allowing the police to use radar guns to detect speeding motorists, since at least it ensures that they're honest: 'It's nice to know that he pulled the trigger on the radar gun and didn't just make up that speed.' But, he feels, individuals should have the right to carry radar detectors. To critics who would say that the radar detector is the driver's equivalent of a burglary tool, Csere 'would simply say that it's very hard to make the case that exceeding the speed limit by five or ten miles per hour is really doing anyone any harm, and for that reason it's really not hurting society. Radar detectors are banned on large trucks because the case has been made that a large truck out of control can do a lot more damage than a passenger car, but in the case of a passenger car a driver should have the right to know when their speed is being monitored in this country by police radar, and that's simply what a radar detector allows you to do.' (He also claims that when the police aren't sure which car they've caught speeding they'll pick on him because he drives a bright red sports car!)

OK, says John Whitelegg, drivers are indeed 'a law-breaking group. They drive over the speed limit, their tyres might not be of the required level of sophistication, the mechanical condition of the car might be defective. Most drivers break the law and the legal system can't cope with that, it's too big a problem. The only solution is technological: taking control of those vehicles from the drivers, controlling the speed, controlling the turning behaviour, and then having a real force of law for deviancy, which is to remove the driving licence and confiscate vehicles.'

But enforcement *can* work, says Alison Smiley, 'if it's frequent. From all the work that's been done on the drink-driving legislation, you find that people will change their behaviour if they are pretty sure that they're likely to run into the police, and the more such a law is enforced the more effective it will be. But that's expensive. Each ticket that a police officer writes takes time, not just in the writing but in the processing, the court action. More and more we are moving either to not enforcing traffic laws or enforcing them through automatic means. A short time ago a police officer said to me something I found quite shocking: he felt that within a few years they wouldn't be enforcing traffic laws. Why? Because they need to devote their time to crime, which the public perceives as the greater need.'

'Enforcement cannot work,' says Dr Bob Davis, chairman of the Road Danger Reduction Forum, 'unless it is far more widespread and unless the public as a whole consider it necessary and desirable to allocate the resources to the police and the courts to carry out their function.' Above all, says John Whitelegg, 'If we're going to make the full force of the law applicable to drivers, there has to be a dramatic shift in public attitudes. That seems to be quite clear. Drivers are insulated from this label of criminality by a sort of popular support. Most of us are drivers, therefore most of us break the law, and law-breakers are not going to turn into advocates for stricter interpretation of the law. But the consequences of law-breaking, in terms of dead children, dead elderly people, serious additional cost to health services and serious disturbance to normal life in cities, is so dramatic that we need to begin public education, an awareness programme. We need to be able to talk to drivers in the same way we talk to drug and alcohol abusers. The abusers of speed and power are on the same level as the abusers of drugs and alcohol, so we need to talk to them in that way and ultimately introduce stiffer penalties. It is being done in Sweden and Denmark already.'

Steve Stradling says, 'Over the last decade or so, there have been some changes in social norms, in Britain and most other Northern European countries. Drink-driving has decreased a lot. Whereas ten years ago the default option was to have a drink and risk it and drive home, now the default option is to take careful and necessary steps to avoid drink-driving, either by not drinking or by using public transport or whatever. So in terms of what we call violating behaviours in general, all the way up to speeding, that's the kind of change that's going to be necessary to bring about large-scale changes of behaviour on the roads.'

TOMORROW

12

Will the Killing Ever Stop?

It is dangerous to be alive but the alternative makes that hazard endurable for most of us. Now that medicine almost guarantees survival for a biblical life-span, the hazards of accidental trauma have become of major concern to the advanced Western countries.

Murray Mackay, Britain's first automobile accident investigator

A morbid friend of mine has a theory that many accidents in Calvinist countries are caused because drivers who see a pedestrian in front of them feel that he or she is predestined to die at this moment and that there is nothing that the driver can do to thwart God's evident will. More seriously a whole theory has evolved that the rate of accidents in any given country tends to improve and then reaches an unhappy, unstable equilibrium. It's only too easy to argue that there is an 'acceptable' level of damage that may be caused by the motor-car, that crashes, like the poor, will always be with us.

The argument goes that there is a normal course of development, which we have already seen in the United States and in Britain: how, in the first 'motorized' generation the crash level is horrendous, but that it gradually diminishes in the course of a single generation to a level we accept as 'normal', as the population adapts itself, in almost Darwinian fashion, to survive in the age of the motor-car.

It is a process that can be compared in some ways with the birth-rate in developing countries. In these places, couples try to produce as many children as possible, partly to help support them in their old age, partly because they expect a high proportion of them to die before reaching adulthood. The first development is that while as many children are born, a higher proportion survives, which provides the impression that over-population will result. But – even in countries which reject contraception – the birth-rate drops steadily in the second generation as parents grow more confident that their offspring will survive. But even in countries that have evolved well beyond this pattern, unwanted children are still conceived. In the same way, we can expect an irreducible number of road accidents.

Leonard Evans of General Motors reassures us that: 'As individuals grow older we know that crash rates decline, a forty-year-old has a substantially lower crash rate than a twenty-year-old, a process that is probably related to the maturation of an individual. There seems to be a parallel process in societies as their average maturation of motorization proceeds: behaviours that are highly risky play a smaller part and the more utilitarian aspect of transportation plays a larger one. To put it on a more personal level, the child who went to kindergarten in a car with his mother is going to have a different attitude regarding the utilitarian aspect of a car compared to some twenty-year-old who has just got the first car the family has ever had.'

The idea that as societies mature and get used to the motor-car accident rates decline to a certain level and then stop falling was first put forward, over thirty years ago, by Reuben Smeed, a mathematician who became the first professor of traffic studies at University College, London. As his successor, John Adams, explains, 'He collected data for a very large number of countries and plotted them on a graph. What he discovered was that there was a relationship between a country's level of motorization and the death rate per motor vehicle. The decrease over time was very large. Going back to the beginning of the century in this country the death rate per vehicle was about thirty times what it is now.

'There are a number of people who seek to claim credit for this. Motor manufacturers say that our vehicles are very much safer than they were at the beginning of the century and therefore they deserve the credit. Highway engineers say our roads are vastly safer than roads at the beginning of the century and therefore they deserve the credit. I think most of the credit goes to the individual road-user and how they modify their behaviour in the face of the dangers that they confront.

'One reason for suggesting this is that if you apply the relationship that Smeed found not to individual countries over time but to a cross-section of countries at one point in time, you find that the same relationship holds. Countries with very few cars today, like countries in West Africa, do not have their own car industry so people drive modern imported cars with eighty or ninety years of safety technology built into them but they drive them in a way that achieves more or less the identical kill rates per vehicle that were being achieved in the early part of this century with Model T Fords. The safety technology hasn't solved the problem. If you live in an African village and have one lorry passing through per week, you don't spend a lot of time drilling your children in the Green Cross code. If you live on the North Circular Road, in London, chances are you won't allow your children out of the front door, so as the threat has increased, as the volume of traffic has increased, I believe that there has been a collective learning experience, and that people have responded in a whole host of ways that they deemed appropriate to the danger that they confront.'

The result is an impressive rate of decline – in the United States the present rate is more than 90 per cent below what it was in 1921, an average decline of about 3.5 per cent per year, which Leonard Evans compares to the steady increase in the human life-span. 'It is because of many things, plumbing, medicine, drugs, surgeons, and in the case of traffic, the answer likewise has many components. There have been improvements in the engineering of the roads and the vehicles, there have been legislative changes, but one of the very big factors is a collective change in driver behaviour.'

In many countries the process is still in its early stages. When Eastern Europe was opened to Western influences, the process of education was speedy, brutal, and dangerous. In Western Europe we can see the process at work most obviously in Portugal. The Portuguese have by far the worst record in Europe, with eighteen times as many deaths as the UK for every mile a car is driven, and three and a half times as many deaths among pedestrians. The driving is dreadful, the roads mostly poor, and even when a new road is built the Portuguese tend to use the hard shoulder as an extra lane – especially dangerous when one heavy lorry is trying to pass another.

The archetype of Portuguese road horror is the route along the south coast in the popular tourist region known as the Algarve. For a start, it fulfils two different functions: it is the major trunk road from the airport to the major tourist spots, but it is also a series of local village streets bordered by restaurants and bars, which are liable to offload drunks on to the road at every hour of the day and night. Capitão Caio, head of the local transport police, says that his biggest problem is drinking and driving, especially among young drivers. There's no separation between the two sides of the road, and it's sometimes dual carriageway, sometimes single lane. In August, the pressure is at its worst as the population swells from four hundred thousand to over two million with the arrival of tourists from all over Europe. There were over two thousand accidents on this one road in the first three months of 1996 – and that was out of season. 'It's an example of a road that should not exist,' says Jose Miguel Trigoso, head of PRP, the official Portuguese road-safety organization. It is used, he says, 'by a mother who's driving with a little daughter to the school two miles away, or by the old lady who needs to cross by foot to go to the supermarket or the grocery. These road-users should not co-exist in the same road infrastructure as all this heavy traffic. This kind of road was very common in Europe some decades ago, and this one is one of the last existing in Portugal with such traffic in the summer period with enormous quantity of tourists.'

The burden of coping with old ladies going shopping while revellers are returning from bars and discos, is typical of a region, which, as Trigoso says, 'is simultaneously tourist and rural and industrial. It's too much for the road, it can't support so many differences between users.'

As he notes shrewdly, 'Our behaviour is extremely influenced by the environment. When you go to a restaurant, for instance, and everything is clean, your behaviour is quite different than if you go to a dirty restaurant. On the road it's the same. When an environment is well organized, when you feel that they thought about your needs when they were preparing it, you behave well but if you drive in an environment where you feel that nobody has thought about you, you don't care and your driving shows that.' Any attempt at reducing the danger seems useless: when they installed speed warning signs the locals took no notice, except for thieves who stole parts of the equipment.

In theory, Portuguese road-safety programmes are run by the PRP, and not by the transport ministry – whose attitude seems unhelpful: one of the people in its office bragged to a television researcher how fast he could drive from the Algarve to Lisbon, claiming that driving fast was not dangerous if you could handle it.

Trigoso, a high-grade professional, accepts that Portugal is going through the same transitional phase that the UK and the USA encountered in the 1950s and 1960s. He attributes Portugal's appalling record to 'the behaviour of the people in the environment' and the type of vehicles and drivers on the roads. More than half of the casualties, he says, 'are not car users. About 55 per cent of road accidents each year involve two-wheeler users and pedestrians. This is unique in the European Union and it's happening, first of all, because there is an enormous number of motorized two-wheelers. Moped riders are mainly young people and workers with a low economic level and they need this kind of vehicle to go to work. The environment is not yet sufficiently well prepared to promote a healthy co-operation between drivers and pedestrians – and more than half of the pedestrians are people over sixty, another problem.

'Compared with other countries in the European Union, in Portugal we have a bigger percentage of new drivers and that means we have more drivers with a lack of experience and with the need to prove that because they own a car they can now do the things that at other times only other people could do. This is a problem that only disappears with time. I think that in the last twenty years the number of cars on the road has grown three or four times, which means that a lot of families have access to a car for the first time. To get all these people driving together on the roads but not competing on them takes time and is one of our problems now.

'They compete on the road. You know, in the last study we did, this year, we made some enquiries here and in another eighteen countries in Europe. Generally, people consider themselves excellent drivers and people who respect others and so on, but they considered that the first cause of accidents is the behaviour of other drivers. This is an enormous problem: that each driver considers [himself] an angel surrounded by a lot of devils causing them enormous problems. This is a situation which makes it enormously difficult to speak to drivers because when, for instance, we organize a campaign through the media, and it's a very strong campaign, the result is that almost everybody tells you, OK, this is a very nice campaign because people need to learn something. That means that the campaign is a disaster because it's not directed at anyone in particular because everyone thinks it's directed to the other drivers, which means to nobody.* It is an extremely difficult task to go directly to the people who are driving or to the users of the roads, so our priority is education but we have been doing this for only two or three years. We started with a new commission which is working with us in our office with people from the Ministry of Education and from the Ministry of Home Affairs to put all the general and specific objectives of road safety education in the normal curriculum and with teachers in the pre-school education and primary education, that means from 3 to 14 years old.'

But Trigoso remains hopeful: today the accident rate 'is now twice what it is in the rest of the European Union but twenty years ago it was four times worse so it is bad but less bad than it was'.

Once Portuguese – and Eastern European – road accidents are down to a 'normal' level, can they be reduced further? Not by technology it seems. Traditionally, says Gerald Wilde, 'the feeling has been that if you could improve technology, education and enforcement, the accident problem would go away, or at least, would diminish very considerably. Now, unfortunately, history has told us otherwise. There is no such a thing as a technological fix for safety because of the way in which people adapt their behaviour to changes in the environment. The technological fix is a myth but we are eager to believe in it because it would be so comfortable if we could just treat the traffic-safety problem with a better road surface or an extra policeman on the road, but the reality is different. Gadgets won't make them live longer. In fact, seat-belts, anti-lock brakes, collapsible steering columns are not safety devices, because of the way people respond to them. They are mobility devices – they enhance mobility – and as mobility is desirable from an economic point of view, these improvements are indeed improvements but you should not call them safety measures.'

---

*A classic instance was that in Prague recently, where the entire safety campaign was called 'a butterfly on your bonnet'. They made two million plastic butterflies, distributed them to schoolchildren to give to their parents, ran advertisements on television and then measured the success of the campaign, not by anything so crude as a reduction in accidents, but by counting the number of people who had noticed the campaign.

Nor, according to Conrad King, is increasing automation any solution. 'Trains are big automated pieces of machinery and still have accidents which tend to be much more horrific because of the number of people and the kind of speeds that are involved. In a perfect world we would have a car we don't need to steer. It has infra-red sensors that prevent you hitting another object. It's able to calculate the speeds of the other cars around you. It's able to take you to your destination and do all of the things in driving that you would normally do. The problem is that no one would want one because you lose your sense of freedom, autonomy, power. That's one of the great things with cars – they make people free.'

This sense of an eventual, unsatisfactory equilibrium is reinforced by the concept of 'accident migration', the idea that when black spots on a road are treated, the accidents will occur further down the road. The treatment reduces not only the accidents but also the fear that accompanies the near misses, which will be far more frequent at an untreated black spot. As Boyle and Wright noted in a 1984 article in the magazine *Traffic Engineering and Control*:

A proportion of drivers leaving an untreated accident black-spot will have been involved in some form of conflict and will be driving more cautiously. Among commuters the effects of a near miss on one day may persist over a long period. Successful treatment of the black spot will reduce the proportion of drivers who are behaving cautiously so that the number of accidents in the surrounding areas will tend to increase towards their 'natural' levels.

Boyle and Wright also produced convincing figures to back up their idea, which sounds like common sense.

Our inability to influence the accident rate is deepened by the way in which the statistical rhythm appears to depend as much on economics as on transport factors. 'The biggest factor to explain the ups and downs in the death rate per head of population,' says Gerald Wilde flatly, 'is the business cycle. When the economy is booming people drive more, people drive faster. They are not so concerned about accidents because cars are relatively cheap to repair, relative to disposable income, and the fuel is relatively cheap. When the economy is booming, the death rate goes up. When the economy is in bad shape, people have less reason to take risks on the road because there's not much money to be made by going there fast anyway.

'So the big factor that explains the drop in the death rate on the roads since, say, the mid-seventies is the oil crisis and the ensuing economic misery from which we still haven't recovered because in terms of disposable income most of the industrialized world is still not as prosperous as it was in the late sixties and in the early seventies. To congratulate ourselves on the improvement in safety per head of population is misleading. Now that the economy is picking up in many nations, the death rate on the road will go up again too. In some countries already, including the United States, there are signs that this is now happening.

'We should look at the picture over a very long term, in a perspective of decades, sometimes half a century. Let's not forget that the death rate in the United States in terms of the number of people killed on the road per hundred thousand citizens was the same in 1987 as it had been in 1927. This is partly because the roads are – or, at least, seem – so safe that people drive a lot. So what you get is a relatively safe activity per mile driven but people drive more and the effect is that, per head of population, the United States is one of the most unsafe countries of the world in terms of the number of people killed per hundred thousand citizens.'

Dr Pat Waller quotes an author who puts the equation in graphic terms: ' "Suppose I could give you a new device that will enable you to get where you want to go rapidly and comfortably and it's just going to open up all kinds of possibilities," and he described the wonderful benefits. But then he said, "In return for this, every year you're going to have to go to the steps of the Washington Monument and sacrifice five thousand young people. Would you be willing to do this in return for this new technology?" People's immediate reaction to that is usually negative, but in effect we're saying we're willing to sacrifice a lot more than five thousand people every year to achieve this mobility. It's well over forty thousand a year in this country at this time.'

'If we were in a war zone,' says Mike Doyle, 'and we were seeing people dying every day, maybe that familiarity would cause it to become acceptable, but we seem to be accepting that accidents will happen. They don't just happen, they're caused. Every accident has a prime cause, whether it's some person's error or whether it's because they're just unable to cope with a situation, but certainly every accident is *caused*. To face death every day, whether it be as a soldier or as a civilian, in a war zone, is bad enough and it seems to become a fact of life – but do we need to make accidents a fact of life?'

Many interviewees felt this same frustration at the lack of any impetus to do better. Everyone involved – the manufacturers, the government, the insurance companies – blames everyone else, says Larry Zeitlin. 'Each accuses the other primarily because no one wants to admit that they're at fault. Cars could be built safer, roads could be built better and, of course, drivers could be better trained. The politics of the situation spreads the blame evenly. The one thing that stops driver training from being improved or safety regulations from being changed is that most people are unwilling to subject themselves to any more discipline and authority than they do now. The thing that stops automobiles from being improved is, of course, the additional cost and that automobile safety, in terms of the vehicle itself, is now reaching a point of diminishing returns. There's not much else one can do with an automobile that will dramatically decrease the accident rate. Of course, the highway factor is based on funding and it is difficult to spend the money necessary to redesign every highway in the country for safety reasons.'

Steve Stradling, too, would 'be amazed if the accident rate ever got reduced to zero. In the UK the number of road fatalities is down to about four thousand deaths a year. Now, that's four thousand deaths too many but it's not at all obvious that it can be reduced much beyond that, it may well have bottomed out.' It is a price that is paid for the advantages offered by the automobile. Not that people make the connection between the advantages and the costs.

The problems are exacerbated by the sheer numbers of people driving cars. As Leonard Evans of General Motors points out, 'A hundred years ago there was no way to predict that such a large proportion of human beings would be able to successfully drive vehicles. In fact, in 1903 Karl Benz said that the world market for automobiles was limited to one million vehicles because there were only one million people who were capable of learning to drive a vehicle. It's very difficult to predict what things people can do. Societies have always had music, and if you didn't know how difficult it was to play the violin you would probably guess that just about anybody could pick it up and reach some modest level of skill without working at it very hard. The reverse is true. But with automobile driving, almost everybody can learn to do it at a reasonable level of proficiency.'

The increasing heterogeneity of drivers creates its own problems. As Stradling points out, 'Initially driving was a wholly male occupation and it was a specialist skill. You had to be a member of a particular élite group to get on the road. It was also a homogeneous group, and one of the core things in road safety is the predictability of other road-users. If you can predict what other people are going to do then you can avoid your trajectory intersecting with theirs. Now, if everybody else on the road is in some sense like you, it's relatively easy to anticipate the kind of thing they are likely to do, but as the mix of people on the roads gets more and more heterogeneous it becomes more difficult to guess what other people are going to do, especially when you get poor information about the demographic characteristics of other drivers. For example, the people behind you – all you can see is a car coming up in the mirror and it's this kind of car so it's likely to be driven by this sort of person, who's going to want to hurry down the outside lane, so they'll want me to move over. You're driving on stereotypes and expectations and on the basis of reduced information.

'It's very difficult to make communication with other drivers. When you're talking face to face with somebody out of the car you have a rich, detailed and, if you're careful, unambiguous communication system. But once you're inside the car it's very basic, and it's like communicating with a small number of grunts, of which each one can mean a variety of things. It's a degraded communication system. When the sun's shining, even with a car coming towards you it's difficult to make out whether it's a male or female, young or old driver. When the car's behind you, you've got very little information. Things are happening very quickly and there's very poor communication. Even when you signal to make a turn it may mean, "I'm going to pull into the side of the road quite soon or in a little while." When the brake light comes on it may mean, "I'm about to stop immediately or I'm slowing down gradually." There's no fine tuning in the signal.

'And, of course, there's no way of saying you're sorry. When things go wrong on the road, if you make a mistake or annoy another driver, there's no clear way of communicating, "Sorry, that was my fault, just a mistake, nothing personal, didn't mean that, just ignore that, yes," and often because of that, situations may be misinterpreted, they can escalate and things can get worse and worse.'

But just look, say the optimists, the trend lines point down. Wait a minute, says Bob Davis, do they mean anything? Who is safe? 'If it's looked at in terms of people who are relatively vulnerable, it may be a great deal more dangerous than the official road-safety establishment makes out. The definition of safety has been made in terms of the criteria set by people who are interested in having more motor traffic on our roads and in terms of pandering to that desire. Every year the official road-safety establishment and the motor manufacturers tell us that things are getting better because the aggregated number of fatalities from road-traffic accidents goes down a little bit. In fact, if you look at total insurance claims, which doubled in the 1980s alone, if you look at the number of reported casualties, which have increased by a hundred thousand since the 1950s, if you look at the chances of being killed when walking and cycling, which haven't significantly gone down at all, you see that the common-sense judgement of people who've lived through the last forty years, that the road environment is now more dangerous, is correct. We do have a more dangerous road environment now, particularly for people who are more vulnerable and people who are outside cars.'

The situation, says John Adams, is 'a rogue's gallery of confusion. A safe road, from a pedestrian point of view, is one in which there is very little traffic or no traffic or traffic going very slowly. A safe road from a road-traffic engineer's or driver's point of view is a road without pedestrians so there's no such thing as safe and dangerous. It depends on your politics and it depends on who is oppressing whom and who is killing whom.'

Sometimes Daniel McCarthy, who as a road safety officer is at the sharp end, doesn't think that things have changed much. He remembers a 1911 poster: 'It was of a chap who was wearing this poster like a sandwich board and it said, 'Men of England, reckless motorists are killing your wives, your children, your dogs and your chickens,' and on a bad day I just think that the only real difference we seem to be making these days is we are killing fewer chickens.'

Forecasts of the inevitability of future mayhem on the roads are often as apocalyptic as those made of world-wide population growth and are often as inaccurate. In 1972 it was predicted that deaths due to traffic accidents could rise to 200,000 per year by the year 2000, and injuries to a million, which was far in excess of reality. Today, international bodies, like the European Union, are setting targets for reducing accidents, although these are relatively modest: the Union hopes to halve road deaths by 2010, which would still leave the death rate in countries like Greece, Portugal and Germany above the level it is at today in Britain or Sweden.

And, as Steve Stradling says, 'All is not lost. The last twenty years have seen some massive cultural shifts. Human beings are adaptable and it gives me hope for the future.'

I have a limited sympathy with the nihilists who argue that all anti-accident activity is pointless, that seat-belts merely transfer the risk, that the considerable reduction in pedestrian casualties is due to the way that pedestrians have removed themselves from the street, that because, tragically, air-bags have caused the death of a handful of children they are not life-savers. People, habits, do change for the better.

As Murray Mackay says, 'There's been tremendous improvements in all dimensions. In the human behaviour area, drinking and driving is now very much lower than it was fifteen years ago, that's been one of the successes. We've got seat-belt use up to 90 per cent or so, that's a behavioural change, another major success. We've got much better highways, in terms of junction design, lighting, barrier design, the control of speed, and we've got much better vehicles than we had a decade or two ago. We can provide much greater survivability, particularly with preventing life-threatening injuries to the head, to the neck, to the chest.'

'I first got into this field in 1967,' says Dr Pat Waller, 'and at that time between five and six people were killed for every hundred million miles that were driven. At that time four was viewed very much like the three-minute mile was viewed, that this was a barrier we would never be able to break. We are now well below two, an accomplishment that I think most people viewed as being essentially impossible back in the late sixties.'

'For a very long time,' says Alison Smiley, 'we accepted the deaths associated with smoking, but gradually people began to say, "Hey, this is too much," and changed legislation and produced education to try to persuade people to stop smoking. The same thing happened with drink-driving. For many years we accepted the fact that 50 per cent of fatal accidents involved alcohol, but then somebody's daughter was killed by a drunk driver and that woman began Mothers Against Drunk Driving, and raised awareness of the size of the problem, to the extent that many people said, "We don't accept this any more," a lot of legislation was introduced to deal with it, and we have seen a decline in the number of fatalities associated with alcohol. I think we need to get to the same point with the whole road-casualty toll. It's simply too high. It is a huge public health problem.'

The most obvious way in which social habits could be changed lies in driver training. Indeed, the degree to which a country is alive to the need to do something about its road-accident record can usually be judged by the seriousness of the driving test. In Libya, for example, it is assumed that the inhabitants don't need to take a test before being let loose on the open road and even in New Zealand the standard of the test leaves a lot to be desired. But in any case it is foolish to assume that a single driving test can cover more than a tiny, and not necessarily representative, sample of the conditions that will be encountered in a lifetime's – or even a year's – driving. Pass the test in a Ford Fiesta in rural Wales and you are automatically entitled to drive a Ferrari on the M1. Test standards are surprisingly low even in the United States, perhaps because driving is considered such a normal occupation. As Csaba Csere says, 'In Michigan, people often don't know that the left [right, in the UK] lane is just for passing on the highways. People don't know how to merge on highways. I think one area where we could really improve in the United States is to have more intensive driver training than we have today.'

The learning process should not consist merely of taking a few lessons, reading up *The Highway Code*, passing a simple written test and then the practical one. It should be more complicated than that, as Steve Stradling explains. His research shows that 'There are three main phases in learning to drive or, perhaps better, becoming socialized into being a member of the driving community. Those three stages are technical mastery, which is learning how to control the vehicle, how to position it on the road and make smooth progress: secondly, reading the road, which is picking up all the clues that are available, both formal things like the road signs and traffic-lights, distances and destinations, but also the informal clues that one learns to recognize – like if you're behind a black cab in the centre of town and he's driving in the middle of the road, you just know he's about to make an unsignalled U-turn and you drive accordingly and allow him the space. But the third stage, which we think, in many ways, is the most important, is the expressive stage, and that's when people are using the manner in which they drive the car to give expression to their personality and their basic attitudes.'

Better training, with the removal from the roads of that relatively small minority of inadequate drivers who cause traffic build-up, blockages, road frustration and, ultimately, road rage would be valuable. Re-tests of drivers should be compulsory after a serious accident, after a conviction for careless driving or worse, and regular after a driver has reached the age of sixty-five.

Recently several innovative ideas have been put forward for reducing the death toll on the roads. Gerald Wilde described one Pavlovian possibility, 'of giving people rewards for accident-free driving. The approach essentially comes out of the world of safety in the workplace where incentives have shown to be an effective way of reducing the accident rate on the shop floor, in mining, in construction, manufacturing, fishing and so forth. There have been cases in North America, also in Europe, where truck drivers were promised that they would get a cash reward or extra holidays for the fact of not having an accident for, say, six months. Under those conditions the accident rate would drop to as much as 50 per cent of what it had been before. Commercial companies have discovered that they can make money on these incentive programmes because not only are the accident rates down but the payments they have to make to workers, compensation boards and other forms of insurance are reduced. They can make money on these incentive programmes, even though they have to give people financial rewards for not having an accident or giving them extra holidays.' In Wilde's view it all hangs on 'the art of reducing the amount of risk people are willing to take on the road.

'Some time ago in California, some 15,000 drivers received a letter saying, "If you don't have an accident for a year from now, we will extend the validity of your driver's licence for free by one year." That was a relatively minor award but it was good enough to result in a 21 per cent reduction in the accident rate of those drivers, as compared to a comparison group that did not receive the letter. In the second year the reduction in the accident rate was actually greater: there were 33 per cent fewer accidents than there were in the comparison group. So the question then arose, how come that in the second year the award was even more effective in producing the desired result of reducing the accident rate than was true in the first year? The interpretation of this difference is that after the first year people discovered that the government meant business with this promise and that the promise was fulfilled and that the incentive programme was not a vacuous bureaucratic ploy.'

A more technocratic approach is to install in cars a 'black box', a recorder similar to those in use in aeroplanes. The device is now being tried out on quite a large scale in Sweden, Germany and in Japan, by manufacturers including Volvo and Mercedes-Benz. 'In the event of an accident,' explains Professor Helmut Rau, 'we can see the impact speed and the velocity before any problems for the driver, and we can see the acceleration, deceleration in case of braking. We also know whether the lights were on. We can see if what the driver has told us happened really happened.'

There is already a version of the black box for sale to private individuals, with a button to enable the driver to delete the data – a temporary device, to help sell the box to the public before it becomes a legal requirement. Even so, says Professor Rau, the mere existence of the box alters drivers' behaviour. The Germans are cautious about the results but, according to Heinz Hubner, the director of police in Berlin, 'Damage during driving to cars equipped with the black box has been reduced. We don't know exactly why yet but I am sure the most important reason that they change their behaviour in traffic is they are more controlled in their driving.' At first, inevitably, 'Policemen didn't like it, we know that, but we did take steps to make clear what we want to do with this and we did say to the police that it's also a protection for their driving. It provides evidence if there is an accident that they are driving correctly.'

In Baltimore some cars have had micro-chips installed which warn a driver if it has been involved in an accident, and, as Dr Burgess explains, 'We're in our next phase of designing cars that have that chip and also record the circumstances of the accident, the change in velocity, the angle of the accident. We'll have an injured patient and the exact circumstances of the accident like a black box in an aircraft. Finally, I think we're going to have in the more civilized countries smart highway systems where cars are directed and accident avoidance is by electronics and radar.'

But for all the bribes, the black boxes, the 'smart systems', in the end it all comes back to driver behaviour. 'We have yet to deal properly with the attitudes and behaviour of the drivers in their responsibility to other road-users,' says road engineer David Silcock.

'Every car on the roads is allegedly within the control of a sane, reasonable and appropriately skilled individual, who is the driver,' says Daniel McCarthy. 'We shouldn't have to continue to try to influence that person by sticking lumps of tarmac in the road to make them go slowly past a school. There should really be some way of contacting them directly and saying, "Look, this is where your children, your friend's children, your neighbour's children go to school. It's incumbent upon you to drive heedful of them." Instead of saying "children were crossing the road heedless of traffic, which caused the accident," we should acknowledge that it was the driver who was driving down that road heedless of children who hit the child and caused the accident. There hasn't been a book written because I think it would be too uncomfortable to actually have to acknowledge that we are the problem. We are the people who are going out and killing ourselves and each other every year, albeit in declining numbers. Regardless of how much energy, effort and money has gone into making cars and roads as safe as they can be, the final piece of the jigsaw religiously refuses to fit into place because drivers will continue to think that in their cars they have *carte blanche* to go out there and be reckless.

'We must get drivers to acknowledge that they are part of a larger society behind the wheel, and that their behaviour behind the wheel directly influences the behaviour of other drivers around them, can seriously compromise and affect the safety of other people around them. We need to get people to be more empathic behind the wheel, to be less self-centred, less dedicated to the pursuits of their own needs, wants and feelings, and explore how they affect other people. We need to get into the minds of drivers and change them to make any sense of safer cars, safer roads. It's a nice idea to think that we could design crashes out of the system but I don't believe the human animal is ever going to be entirely trustworthy if left wholly at liberty to control a motor vehicle.'

The first step in changing human behaviour must be to stop thinking in terms of accidents and to talk exclusively of crashes. Indeed, many of our interviewees harped on the point: accidents are accidental while crashes have a cause or causes. 'The automobile,' says Leonard Evans of GM, 'is used for suicide and it's used for homicide, though not as much as it is in the movies. To use the word accident seems to separate the car from the actions of the driver who was involved. Often the word accident is used to deny responsibility. Crash is a more objective word in that you report what you observed and later you can delve more closely into whether it was or was not in ordinary common terms an accident. This is the pattern used in civil aviation. We talked about the crash of PanAm 103 even before we knew whether or not, in ordinary parlance, it was an accident.'

'The word accident,' says Daniel McCarthy, 'implies that nothing could be done and we can all walk away from it feeling that we gave it our best shot and the inevitable happened. Perhaps we ought to take more account of the fact that accidents are human-related, and they're almost inevitable so long as people continue to think about cars and choose to drive cars in the way they currently do.'

'Every one is caused,' says Mike Doyle. 'They don't just happen. People and machinery cause accidents and the greatest proportion of accidents are caused by people. Machinery and vehicles are extremely reliable.'

'We like to think that crashes are not inevitable,' says Dr Pat Waller, 'and indeed we refer to them as crashes rather than accidents to convey the idea that this is something that you can do something about.'

In the end, any real improvement is up to us, the road-users.

Select Bibliography

Richard Sutton, *Motormania*
(Collins & Brown, London, 1996)

John Cohen & Barbara Preston, *Causes & Prevention of Motor Accidents*
(Faber & Faber, London, 1968)

William Plowden, *The Motor Car & Politics 1896–1970*
(Bodley Head, London, 1971)

Bill Morris, *Biography of a Buick*
(Granta, London, 1992)

Ralph Nader, *Unsafe at Any Speed*
(First published by Grossman, USA, in 1972. 2nd edn, Knightsbridge
Publishing Company, New York, USA, 1991)

Marsh & Collett, *Driving Passion: the Psychology of Driving*
(Cape, London, 1986)

John Adams, *Risk*
(Taylor & Francis, London, 1995)

Mayer Hillman, John Adams, John Whitelegg, *One False Move: A Study of
Children's Independent Mobility*
(Policy Studies Institute, London, 1991)

John D. Graham, *Autosafety*
(Auburn House Publishing, Dover, Massachusetts, USA, 1989)

Index

182

INDEX

183

INDEX